. . . From time immemorial, man has insisted on venturing into the unknown despite his inability to predict precisely the value of any given exploration. He has been willing to take risks, willing to be surprised, willing to adapt to new experiences. Man has come to feel that such quests are worthwhile in and of themselves—for they represent one way in which he expands his vision and expresses the human spirit. A great nation must always be an exploring nation if it wishes to remain great.

March 7, 1970   RICHARD M. NIXON

NASA SP-250

THIS ISLAND

Edited by

Scientific and Technical Information Division
OFFICE OF TECHNOLOGY UTILIZATION   1970
NATIONAL AERONAUTICS AND SPACE ADMINISTRATION
Washington, D.C.

EARTH

ORAN W. NICKS

FOREWORD

In the accelerating pace of scientific advance, perspective is often a casualty. In less than a decade of space progress, such an avalanche of events occurred that the individual mileposts are difficult to recall.

Men walked the surface of the Moon, brought back the material from another body in space, and emplaced sensitive scientific experiments that continued to report after the men returned to Earth. Scientific satellites mapped the particles and fields of near-Earth space, and made new discoveries about the Sun and the stars. Unmanned spacecraft were flown close to Mars and Venus, returning a rich harvest of imagery and data from these other worlds more than scores of millions of miles distant. All this occurred in short compass, and similar trail-blazing events are scheduled for the decade of the 70's.

New frontiers have always been a catalyst for civilization's advances. Historians of our country have credited much of our people's energy and exuberance, inquisitiveness and daring, inventiveness and initiative, to the challenge of geographical frontiers. Some have feared that the settlement and development of the western states marked the end of the nation's youthfulness and that the fresh, confident outlook might never come again. But now a new frontier has been opened, the frontier of space. This frontier provides a renewed stimulus for our nation's growth, and does so with noble motivation: exploration of the unknown, expansion of knowledge, and unselfish sharing of the new for the betterment of all.

This book is concerned with our home planet, in perspective with its neighborhood in the solar system. It is somewhat paradoxical that man's new ability to fly above the atmosphere and voyage in space has provided him with a new and valuable way to appreciate his Earth. From orbital altitudes the eye and lens do not see the emotions and passions that daily concern mankind on the surface. Economic, political, and sociological tensions are invisible. But the changes that both natural and human forces bring about on the Earth's surface can best be grasped from the respectful distances inherent in Earth orbits. Photographs such as this book contains increase our understanding of the relationships between our activities and our environment.

The world of the 1970's will be vastly different from the world of the 1960's, and many of the changes in it will result directly from the new perspective that we have suddenly acquired. The world of the 1980's will be even more different. By heeding the lessons learned in the last decade, and attacking our many problems with the same spirit, determination, and skill with which we have ventured into space, we can make "this island Earth" a better planet on which to live.

October 1970

GEORGE M. LOW,
Acting Administrator,
National Aeronautics and
Space Administration

PREFACE

THIS BOOK WAS INSPIRED by the words of Apollo astronauts Borman, Lovell, and Anders, who saw and described the Earth as a planet at Christmastime, 1968. Their eyewitness accounts impressed millions of men with the true reality of our situation: the oneness of mankind on this island Earth, as it floats eternally in the silent sea of space.

An extension of this experience is offered by this volume. It is an attempt to project the true perspective of our island and our existence on it, by presenting photographs of Earth taken from space, primarily by Apollo spacecraft. Although many of the photographs and much of the information here have scientific significance, the book was written to share with all men a major benefit of our nation's space program—a sobering realization of man's place in the universe.

Were photographs of Earth from beyond the vicinity of the Moon available, they would have been helpful in achieving perspective. It was necessary, however, to call on imagination to portray the awesome insignificance of the Earth when compared to the giant planets of our solar system, and to show our island home as it would appear if it were approached from another star. Not until an explorer came relatively close to Earth and Moon, in orbit together around the Sun, would the differences between them become apparent. And not until detailed observations had been made from low Earth orbit would the hand of man be evidenced. Most of this book is devoted to the closer view from orbit, and that view was restricted to a relatively few orbits at low latitudes. Even so, the pictures clearly show the wonders and resources available to man. In some we are reminded of the limitations of these resources, and of the impact that man is having on his environment.

The astronauts' descriptions from space, the pictures returned from space, and the strong desire to share these experiences with others have led to the preparation of this book. Like many NASA undertakings, it was a team effort. Several individuals set aside personal identities, contributing gladly as captives to an exciting cause. Most planning was done in conference; individual efforts were shaped and completed by the group. The team itself can hardly be defined in limited terms, for it must be thought of as including all the thousands who made possible its contents.

Many of that team are now engaged in planning and preparing the continuing exploration and use of space. Missions to Mars, continuing flights to the Moon, and developments leading to operations in Earth orbit occupy major programs. The emphasis on transportation for low-cost flights to and from space will surely further the activities of man in expanding his neighborhood to the nearby planets. In a humanistic sense there is no turning back; already the Moon must be accepted as part of the province of all men, in the way that Hawaii and Alaska are no longer remote outposts but are irrevocably a part of these United States.

October 1970   ORAN W. NICKS,
                Acting Associate Administrator,
                Office of Advanced Research
                and Technology

ACKNOWLEDGEMENTS

THIS BOOK WAS ENABLED by the thousands of people directly and indirectly at work on the American program for the exploration of space. It was conceived, planned, and produced by a smaller but still large group of persons, mainly but not solely within the National Aeronautics and Space Administration, who wished to share with others the beauty and excitement of new perspectives about the planet Earth.

To aid in producing this book, Melvin S. Day, Acting Assistant Administrator for Technology Utilization, lent to its editor the services of the Scientific and Technical Information Division, directed by John F. Stearns. Design and production were done by Rex Matthews, Sandra Scaffidi, and Kay Voglewede. Writers were Wesley S. Griswold, Frank Rowsome, Jr., and Volta Torrey.

Technical counsel in specific areas was provided by a much larger group, which included Michael Amajian, Frank W. Anderson, Jr., Herbert Blodget, William Brunk, Edgar M. Cortright, John M. DeNoyer, Les Gaver, Edwin C. Kilgore, Paul D. Lowman, Benjamin Milwitzky, John E. Naugle, Henry J. Smith, Richard Underwood, Margaret Ware, and Edward Zeitler, all of NASA. Donald R. Baker, E. Paul McLain, Stanley D. Soules, and Alan E. Strong of the National Environmental Satellite Center provided information and guidance. Professors Jerome D. Lettvin, Harold E. Edgerton, and Carroll L. Wilson of the faculty of the Massachusetts Institute of Technology supplied helpful assistance. Professor Robert N. Colwell of the University of California at Berkeley contributed guidance about the Apollo 9 photographic experiment. John F. McCauley and Elliott C. Morris of the U.S. Geological Survey gave both counsel and assistance.

John Hall of the Lowell Observatory, Gerard P. Kuiper of the Lunar and Planetary Laboratory of the University of Arizona, and Ermine van der Wyk of the Jet Propulsion Laboratory were all of aid in numerous respects.

John Caffrey of the American Council on Education gave permission to quote from his letter to *Science*. The Harvard University Press granted permission to use the quotation from *Earth, Moon and Planets* by Professor Fred Whipple. The quotation from Wilfred Thresiger was used with the permission of the copyright holder, E. P. Dutton & Co., Inc. The newsphoto on page 36 was supplied by AP Wirephoto.

It is perhaps unnecessary to note that any deficiencies in this book are not the responsibility of those numerous people who so generously lent their expertise on particular parts of it.

For sale by the Superintendent of Documents, U.S. Government Printing Office, Washington, D.C. 20402—Price $6.00

Library of Congress Catalog Card No. 73–608969

CONTENTS

AS11-36-5345

Closing in on the cloud-whorled blue planet Earth, a traveler arriving from deep space would observe that its surface is predominantly water, as seen in this view of the Pacific Ocean. It is late afternoon in western North America (upper right), and near midday the following day in Australia (lower left). At the top, the north polar cap gleams white.

2

1
Near a Star Called Sun

To see the Earth as it truly is, small and blue and beautiful in that eternal silence where it floats, is to see ourselves as riders on the Earth together, brothers on that bright loveliness in the eternal cold— brothers who know now that they are truly brothers.
—ARCHIBALD MacLEISH

A PERSON STROLLING through a flower garden, enjoying the colors and fragrances, perceives a very different reality than does an ant hurrying along in the dirt, or a hawk lazily orbiting high above. Each living creature sees a reality that is only part of the whole, a coexisting segment that reflects the sensors that make the perception, and their position and field of vision. Whether the reality perceived is a flower garden or a planet, a new point of view can give freshly illuminating insights, as conducive to understanding as the panorama revealed to the first prehistoric man who scaled a mountain and thereby sensed the position of his home valley in the scheme of things. The new art of space exploration has many rewards, but few are as profound as the rich new perspective we have gained about the planet Earth.

At the beginning of the 1970's, 12 men and a handful of automated spacecraft have looked back at Earth from distances as great as the orbit of its natural satellite, the Moon. Some of the images their lenses have captured, taken at ranges approaching a quarter of a million miles, are reproduced on these pages. The full impact that these pictures have had, and will have in the years to come, can only be imperfectly understood. British astrophysicist Fred Hoyle predicted as long ago as 1948: "Once a photograph of the Earth, taken from the outside, is available—once the sheer isolation of the Earth becomes plain—a new idea as powerful

as any in history will be let loose." Some of the influence of Earth photography was suggested in the letters column of *Science* on March 20, 1970, when John Caffrey wrote in part:

> . . . I date my own reawakening of interest in man's environment to the Apollo 8 mission and to the first clear photographs of the Earth from that mission. My theory is that the views of the Earth from that expedition and from the subsequent Apollo flights have made many of us see the Earth as a whole, in a curious way— as a single environment in which hundreds of millions of human beings have a stake.
>
> One view in particular is awe-inspiring— with Africa in the foreground and the whole profile of the Mediterranean very clear. One stares at the whole Mediterranean, looking from outer space much as in an atlas, but not as in a drawing. Much of our most commonly taught history centers around that little sea, a mere patch of the hemisphere, which once seemed to its inhabitants to be the whole world.
>
> Looking at the blackness beyond the sharp blue-green curve, trying to see even the place where the thin envelope of atmosphere and the solid Earth meet, the curious word "fragile" comes to mind. To be on Earth and think of it as fragile is ridiculous. But to see it from out there and to compare it with the deadness of

3

HIGH ALTITUDE OBSERVATORY The star called Sun is surrounded by a streaming, radiant corona observed here during a total solar eclipse. To compensate for the brightness range, this picture, made by Gordon Newkirk, Jr., was shot through a radially graded filter.

the Moon! I suspect that the greatest lasting benefit of the Apollo missions may be, if my hunch is correct, this sudden rush of inspiration to try to save this fragile environment—the whole one—if we still can.

Perspectives have a way of shifting, nevertheless, and the scale of man's aspirations can enlarge at great speed. Last decade's giant step for mankind will almost certainly be remembered by future generations as an historic action, but the scale of the event may be diminished before the century is out. In the immensity of space, the Moon is very close to the Earth, and the first manned lunar landing may come to seem, in the ocean analogy that comes so easily to us, as essentially similar to the paddling out by three valiant men in a dugout canoe to explore for the first time the nearest offshore island. Homer Newell, NASA's Associate Administrator,

4

has said that the solar system is becoming the neighborhood of man, and in the solar system we will encounter depths of distance and durations of time that will make the ocean parallel even more apt.

One way to see our neighborhood with a fresh eye is to approach it from afar. In fancy, let us assume that a spacecraft is approaching the solar system after a voyage across the inconceivable vastness of interstellar space. We may imagine—the details are not critical to the figure—that it carries extraterrestrial beings from a planet in orbit around Alpha Centauri B, 4.3 light-years away. They are creatures of a carbon-oxygen-hydrogen life form, entering the third millennium of scientific life on their home planet, and they have undertaken a hazardous and costly voyage for four powerful reasons. The first is that their scientists, studying a star later found to be called Sun and rivaling Sirius in brightness, have concluded that although

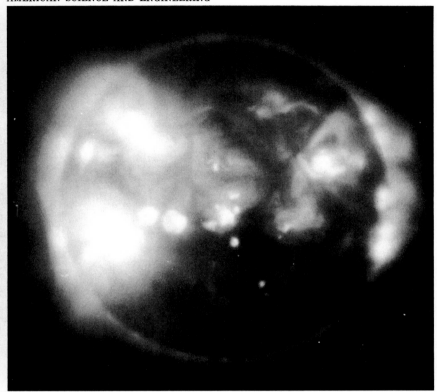

This glowering view of the Sun's X-ray activity was captured by an X-ray telescope, rocket borne above the filtering atmosphere. Note the large, looping structures, like force fields, of X-radiation.

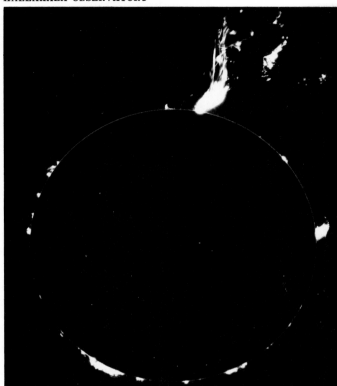

A spray flare event on the Sun, on March 1, 1969. Solar flares can arise in minutes, and spend several hours in slow decay.

25 280 000 000 000 miles distant, it is nevertheless their nearest neighbor in the Galaxy. Very careful observation of the bright star's apparent movement might have led to a second reason for the voyage: such motion can be most reasonably explained by the presence around it of invisible planets of significant mass, and it is only on such bodies that the strange phenomenon of replicating organic cells called life can be imagined to exist. A third reason is that they have lately detected peculiar electromagnetic radiation from the vicinity of the bright star— radiation having a degree of organization that, their savants feel, is not easily explained by random mechanisms. The last and most powerful reason why they are aboard this space ark is that they have just lately achieved the technology that makes exploration to the vicinity of the bright star possible. As seekers of knowledge they believe deeply that there is an imperative to investigate the possi-

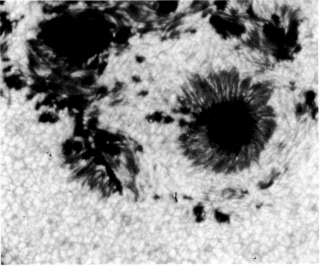

PROJECT STRATOSCOPE

The lowest visible part of the Sun's atmosphere is granular and constantly changing. Sunspots, which are slightly less hot, may have lifetimes of months.

5

ble, as well as to learn all that can then be learned.

Our oncoming visitors from the vicinity of Alpha Centauri must be assumed to have at their disposal a body of knowledge and technology at least equivalent to that prevailing on Earth, our societal health permitting, at the beginning of the next century. (If they did not, it is difficult to see how they could be coming here.)

What would they see with their spaceborne instrumentation as they raced toward the Sun through the cold distances of interstellar space? In the Milky Way—our home Galaxy—the Sun is just one of more than 100 billion other stars, a "grain of sand on the celestial beach." This almost inconceivable agglomeration of stars is disk shaped, about 90 000 light-years in diameter and much less in thickness, rotating in its entirety. Though located well off from the center, the Sun is, so far as can be judged, comfortingly average in characteristics: it is larger than some stars but smaller than others, hotter than some but cooler than others. It is somewhat less than 5 billion years old, which makes it middle aged; it is still near the middle of the main life sequence of the many great hydrogen-fusion reactors in the heavens. Our star is too young, by some billions of years, for the cataclysmic degenerative processes that mark the death of stars. In color, too, the Sun is remarkably middle of the road, located at a yellow-white intermediate point between the fierce blue-white of the hottest and the dim red of the coolest visible stars. Seeking perspective rather than disparagement, philosopher Alfred North Whitehead once said we live on "a second-rate planet revolving about a second-rate Sun." It is a verdict that may have served Whitehead's need in context but also may be unjust to our star and planet. Man can think of very few ways in which the Sun might be changed that would not be disadvantageous to the life that has evolved on its third planet.

No Mean Star

No one should infer from our Sun's apparent averageness that it is tame and docile. Far from it: the Sun is a raging nuclear reactor 870 000 miles in diameter that consumes more than 4 tons of its mass every second. It is the dominant source of the Earth's energy; all of our food and all of our fossil fuels are products of solar energy. Every living thing, including man, is intimately dependent on it. The Sun emits not just visible light but all other kinds of electromagnetic radiation, including X-rays. It sends out streams of high-energy particles that can only be feebly mimicked by the biggest accelerators on Earth. It has a complex and turbulent atmosphere, strong magnetic fields, and an enveloping corona—the pearly high-temperature plasma that is the Sun's outer atmosphere—which extends for millions of miles before it becomes the pervasive solar wind, made up of energetic particles that rush out beyond Earth 92 956 000 miles away. Typical though it may be, our star is no mean thing.

Our visitors would have to come relatively close before they could positively detect what may (or may not) be an *un*average characteristic of the Sun—its complex system of circling planets. Mathematicians have calculated that, at a distance of just under half a light-year, a 60-inch spaceborne telescope might just be able to detect Jupiter, the largest of the Sun's planets, although it would be very difficult to differentiate its image from that of the background of similar faint objects. Jupiter would not show as a disk until the distance had narrowed to 90 astronomical units. (The astronomical unit is the distance of the Earth from the Sun.) The blue-white disk of the little planet Earth might be distinguished at about 7.6 astronomical units. As the explorers drew close enough to see the solar system in full, an extraordinary sight would unfold, a complex Newtonian orrery of masses in motion, tethered by invisible gravitational leashes. Somehow the bright star Sun has acquired an assemblage of nine highly varied spheres, some clearly solid and others veiled in gases, each revolving about the star at a different distance and velocity. They sweep very nearly but not quite the same planes; they orbit in ellipses that, in the main, are nearly but not quite circles. Most of them not only revolve around the Sun but also rotate about polar axes, variously tilted; a few have lost or have been deprived of this independent axial rotation and are locked into externally governed rotation. Even more remarkably, at least six of the Sun's nine spheres have satellites of their own. At least 32 such bodies encircle planets in an intricate grand design of subsystems within the solar system.

Confronted with this strange and beautiful family that the bright star has in attendance, our Cen-

CATALINA OBSERVATORY

Jupiter, the dominant planet in the solar system, has been intensively studied but is not well understood. The elliptical scar in the upper third of this 1968 Ektachrome is the Great Red Spot. The black disk below is the shadow of the satellite Io, barely visible as a lighter-colored object 3.5 cm to the right. In the photo at right, the four largest of Jupiter's 12 satellites are shown orbiting their planet, as in a miniature solar system. It was such a view that gave Galileo a clear concept of our Earth's place among the planets.

LOWELL OBSERVATORY

7

taurian explorers might pull up above the plane of the ecliptic, and cruise at more modest speed while investigating the Sun's planets, truly a *novus ordo seclorum.*

The Loneliest Known Outpost

The planetary positions at the time of approach (and the characteristics of the Centaurian sensors, animate and inanimate) would determine what the visitors would notice first. It would probably not be Pluto, although this is the Sun's farthest and loneliest known planetary outpost. This Earth-sized body patrols an elliptical orbit some 3600 million miles from its primary, so remote from the fire that its temperature is only —350° F, traveling so far and so slowly that it needs almost two and a half centuries to complete one Plutonian year. Even if perceived, it would not be likely to win close attention, for in the phrase of a Harvard astronomer, Fred Whipple, Pluto is "inhospitable beyond comprehension."

Far more likely to attract attention from Centaurian explorers are the next four planets; each one of them is a strange, forbidding, gas-enveloped giant. The outer pair, Neptune and Uranus, are very nearly twins, about 29 000 miles in diameter (Earth's diameter is 7927 miles). Neptune could win notice because it has two singularly different satellites. One is very large, bigger and nearer its primary than Earth's Moon, whereas the other is a speck of something a few hundred miles in diameter, orbiting at a distance of almost 3.5 million miles. Puzzlingly, the little moon travels in conventional, direct rotation while the big inner moon moves in retrograde direction. Anomalies like this, of which the solar system has a plentiful supply, are intellectual challenges to those who would devise acceptable theories of how our worlds came to be.

Uranus is another greenish-white giant, cold and mysterious. It has five satellites—Ariel, Umbriel, Titania, Oberon, and Miranda. What might interest explorers most is the remarkable tilt of its axis, which is almost 98° to its orbital plane. Uranus is a planet that travels about the Sun spinning rapidly on its side.

Intriguing though these frigid and distant objects are, Centaurian visitors would probably find the next two gas-enveloped giants even more so. Saturn is immense, more than 75 000 miles in diam-

eter, greenish-yellow in color. Perceived from a distance near the limits of instrumental resolution, Saturn first appears oddly lumpish. Drawings of it made by observers on Earth using the first Galilean spyglasses show it as a peculiar, jug-eared object, almost like an ancient ewer. With better instruments, or, in the case of visitors, decreasing distance, the reason for the shape would become clear. Professor Whipple has described our view of it from Earth in this way:

> . . . *Among the innumerable celestial objects that may be seen through a telescope, the most beautiful of all is perhaps the planet Saturn. When viewed in the evening twilight while the sky is still bright, the yellow gold ball and its unbelievable rings shimmer in a brilliant blue medium, more like a rare work of art than a natural phenomenon. Lightly shaded surface bands, more uniform than those of Jupiter, parallel the great rings; only occasionally can one distinguish detailed markings that will reveal the rapid turning of the great globe. The central brilliance fades away toward the hazy limb of the planet's disk, and the rings at their borders appear to dissolve into the sky.*

These strange rings are unique in the solar system. Their greatest diameter is 171 000 miles and they are so thin that they almost disappear from view when presented edge on. Early thickness estimates of a few miles have recently been reduced; they may be much thinner. The inner and outer edges are tenuous enough for brighter stars to be seen through them. Although appearing like washer-shaped disks, we know from some intellectually elegant spectroscopic observations that they cannot be rigid objects. The doppler shift shown by a spectroscope reveals that the outer edge of a ring does not have the same period of revolution as the inner, which it would have to if the ring were a solid object. Instead, the outer edge has a lesser velocity than the inner, in exact obedience to the Keplerian laws of motion. Thus the rings are discontinuous, a flat swarm of particles, each one a tiny satellite of Saturn. Their spectroscopic signature resembles that of hoarfrost, and they may be pulverized, icy grit, set in motion by some cataclysmic event in the planet's past. Saturn also has 10 moons of its own, making it almost a miniature solar system. Titan,

Saturn, a banded gold globe encircled by icy-white rings, was photographed on Ektachrome on October 14, 1968, by the 61-inch telescope at Catalina Observatory. The geometrically perfect rings are Saturn's hallmark. Two inner rings, too faint to be photographed, have also been observed.

the largest of these satellites, is not only bigger than Earth's Moon but larger than the planet Mercury. It is the only satellite in the solar system that is known to have an atmosphere, which seems to be methane. As with Neptune, one of Saturn's satellites moves in the puzzling retrograde direction. Several of its satellites have a captured axial rotation, like that of our Moon. One of these, Iapetus, is peculiar. It is five times more reflective on one side than on the other, for reasons we can only speculate about. Was it disfigured by some immense collision? Was it blackened by some sudden burst of Saturnian energy?

Monstrous Storms on Jupiter

The next planet inward is Jupiter, 484 million miles from the Sun, a formidable gas-enveloped object with a mass some 318 times that of the Earth. Its mass, more than twice that of all the other planets put together, wields a perturbing in-fluence in the solar system second only to that of the Sun. It is a yellow-white ball about 86 000 miles in diameter, whirling on its axis every 9 hours and 55 minutes, a velocity that bulges its equator and flattens its poles. Jupiter is a highly dynamic planet. It has a strong magnetic field, estimated at more than 10 times that of Earth, and is a powerful emitter of radio noise on many different frequencies. (Some noisy bursts from Jupiter bear a curious resemblance, in electromagnetic signature, to monstrous lightning storms.) Jupiter radiates significantly more energy than it receives from the Sun, indicating that, in the immense pressures of its interior, gravitational or thermonuclear transformations are at work.

By telescope from the Earth, Jupiter shows a dense atmosphere arranged in slate-blue and salmon-pink bands parallel to the equator. Hydrogen is a main element in its atmosphere, although there are also indications of methane and ammonia.

9

When it rains or snows on Jupiter, it may rain or snow ammonia. No man has ever seen the surface of the planet, if there is one. Some vortices in the atmosphere move at supersonic speeds. Peculiar recurrent markings drift about the atmosphere. For more than 300 years, men have watched the Great Red Spot, an elliptical mark 25 000 miles long and 8000 miles wide, that wanders somewhat in latitude and a great deal in longitude. Much ingenuity has been devoted to trying to understand the Great Red Spot, which might be a convective column of some combination of gases. Nobody really knows what it is.

As befits its immense mass, Jupiter has collected 12 moons, the largest assemblage of satellites in the solar system. The four most distant ones, orbiting some 14 million miles out, have retrograde movement; the other eight do not. Galileo discovered four of the inner ones with his primitive spyglass in 1609. They can readily be seen from Earth with binoculars and could in fact be seen without, save for the veiling glare of the planet nearby. Three of them, Io, Ganymede, and Callisto, are larger than our Moon; and Ganymede is so large that it should have retained an atmosphere, although none has been detected. The inner four circling moons, eclipsing and being eclipsed by Jupiter, are one of the most rewarding sights in the solar system. Astronomers have long been intrigued by them. In 1675 Danish astronomer Rømer noticed an apparent irregularity in the orbital periods of these satellites. He correlated it with changes in the distance between Jupiter and Earth, and deduced that light could not be instantaneous, as previously thought, but must have a finite velocity, which he calculated quite accurately. It was a remarkable intellectual feat, and a brilliant demonstration of the power of reason.

A Swarm of Asteroids

Jupiter's great mass and strong gravitational pull may have done more than sweep up its large family of satellites. Some theoreticians of the origins of the solar system—the archeologists of astronomy— assign to Jupiter a role in achieving the remarkable closeness of the planes of the Sun's planets. It is a closeness unlikely to have been achieved by chance; the greatest departures from the plane of the solar system are made by Pluto and Mercury, the outer-

most and innermost, farthest from Jupiter's influence. Another pondered effect of Jupiter may lie inward from the giant planet, around 260 million miles from the Sun. Here, where we should expect to find a planet, by the rough spacing expressed as Bode's law, we find instead a swarm of asteroids.

Like so much else in the new neighborhood of man, the asteroids are cryptic. Ceres, the largest, is a world 480 miles in diameter; Pallas is 304 miles, Vesta 240 miles. We do not know whether solar-system explorers would be likely to see the asteroids as a belt; perhaps not, because from Earth only a dozen or so asteroids can be seen as disks in a telescope, and the remainder are pinpricks of light. Some have a regularly varying brightness, suggesting that they are not spherical but irregular, mountain-sized fragments of tumbling rock. There may be 50 000 or more of these relatively small objects. Only one, Vesta, has ever been seen by the unaided eye; the preponderance have been discovered by photography. While it is tempting to interpret this swarm of planetoids as the fragments of an archaic planet remaining after some calamitous event, the difficulty is that there do not seem to be enough fragments: the total mass of all asteroids is estimated to be only 1/3000th that of Earth. Another theory, also unsatisfactory in some aspects, is that they might represent preplanetary material that, because of the gravitational pull of Jupiter, never managed to condense into a planet. When the asteroids can be studied and sampled, they may cease to be enigmas and become important keys to planetary history. They may also serve a different purpose; imaginative engineers have calculated that some asteroids would be useful as space bases, large enough to afford protective shelter, small enough to exert only negligible gravity, with attendant low-energy demands for arrivals and departures.

It is convenient at this point to make some assumptions about the way in which extraterrestrial explorers would plan a reconnaissance of the solar system. The first assumption is that life seeks life or a suitable place for it. The second is that the outer planets, for all their fascinating phenomena, are so intensely cold and so wreathed in noxious atmospheres that the Centaurians might not expect to find life on them. It is on the inner planets that the search would most reasonably be concentrated, for it is there that surface temperatures fall into ranges that are least jarring to our concept of life.

We can further envision the visitors limiting their search by making a quick scan from afar of Mercury, the innermost and thus most Sun-baked planet. It is a small, dense body with little or no atmosphere and faint, ambiguous surface markings. Radar studies of it from Earth suggest only modest surface roughness. Mercury's rotation was long believed to be locked on the Sun, always presenting the same face to that thermonuclear caldron a mean 35.9 million miles away. But radar has shown us that this was an illusion, and its rotation is in fact about 58 days. What deceived terrestrial observers

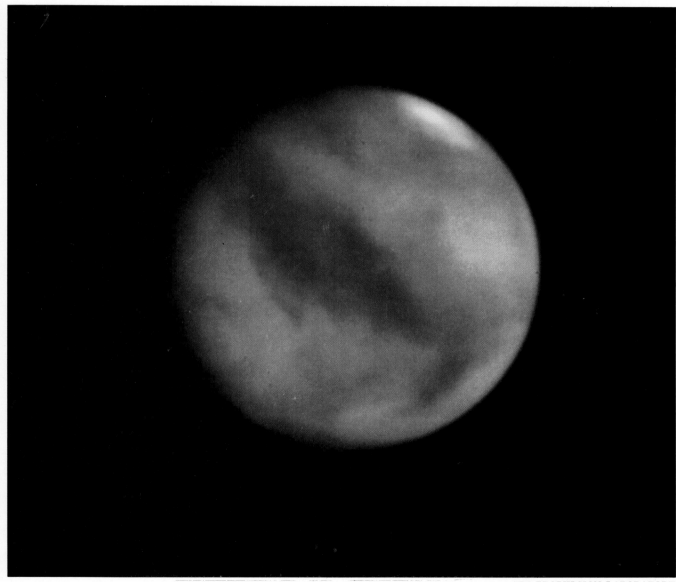

JET PROPULSION LABORATORY

This is one of the best color images of Mars ever obtained from Earth. It was taken in August 1956 by Robert B. Leighton of the California Institute of Technology. It was a 20-second exposure on Kodachrome Type A, using the 60-inch Mount Wilson reflector cut to 21 inches. The south polar cap is at the top.

11

  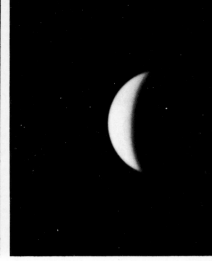

Tantalizingly, Venus is best lighted for viewing from the Earth when it is farthest away, and most poorly lighted when it is nearest. The distance of Venus from Earth varies from a closest approach of about 26 million miles to 160 million miles

for so long—aside from the faintness of the markings—was the fact that the 58-day rotation is close to two-thirds of its 88-day period of solar revolution. This meant that observers frequently looked at the same area at times of most favorable viewing. With radiometric temperatures on the sunlit face approaching 640° F, it is easy to anticipate a Centaurian decision, based on dwindling consumables and an assessment of probabilities, to concentrate on the Sun's remaining planets: Mars, Venus, and Earth/Moon.

Scouting the Red Planet

Ruddy-colored Mars is very cold at night and in winter, perhaps —100° F, or colder, but daytime temperatures in summer may reach 70° F. Through the thin, transparent atmosphere, white polar caps may be seen. Although the visitors might not have the time to perceive it, Mars has a seasonal cycle of expansion and contraction of the polar caps, and a wave of darkening that diffuses from the shrinking cap. The planet also has weather of a sort, including occasional clouds and duststorms driven by tenuous, high-velocity winds. Two tiny moons perhaps only 10 miles in diameter encircle Mars, and the inner one, Phobos, is abnormally close. To an observer on Mars, Phobos would rise and set twice each night, rising in the west and setting in the east. Scanning instruments aboard a visiting spacecraft might show the terrain to be highly variable, in many places pocked with craters, in others free of any markings at all, and in others chaotically tumbled, as though some substance had been drawn out from beneath until the crust collapsed. The dominant compound in the atmosphere as well as in the

white polar caps would show spectroscopically as carbon dioxide; only minute quantities of water would be detected.

Turning their sensors toward Venus, the second planet orbiting in the bright star's habitable zone, the visitors would find a challenge to the sensitivity and resolution of their instruments. Venus is a near sister to the Earth in diameter and density, and travels in an almost perfectly circular orbit 67.2 million miles from the Sun. (At times only 25 million miles from Earth, it appears from our planet to be the brightest object in the sky after the Sun and Moon. It can sometimes be seen in daylight by those who know where to look, and has doubtless contributed its share to flying-saucer sightings.)

In the light of some interpretations, Venus may have preceded Earth in the evolution of its atmosphere, but if the analogy is applicable, something terribly wrong took place, for Venus has a dense, deep atmosphere, seemingly carbon dioxide. As a result of the greenhouse effect—a trapping process by which incoming heat radiation passes through the atmosphere more readily than it can be reradiated—Venus appears to be far hotter than its solar distance would suggest, perhaps approaching 1000° F. Metallic minerals on Venus' surface may glow dull red, and metals like zinc and tin would be liquids. The rotational period of this baffling planet has long been uncertain to man, because the dense bright clouds offer no reliable reference mark. Recently, though, high-powered radars have penetrated the opaque shroud of carbon dioxide, revealing the astonishing fact that Venus turns very slowly in a retrograde direction, once every 243 days. The timing of this rotation, in relation to orbital conjunction with Earth, leads to the

12

at maximum separation. Some indication of its extraordinarily dense, almost light-piping atmosphere can be gained from the last image. This series was collected over many years at the Lowell Observatory in Flagstaff.

A striking similarity between volcanic features on the Moon and Earth is apparent in the paired pictures below. The photo at bottom left was taken by Lunar Orbiter 5 over the Marius Hills. The picture at bottom right is a side-looking radar image of a fissure cone and a breached cone in an Arizona volcanic field. A fissure cone is a volcanic vent along a linear fracture; a breached cone is one in which upwelling lava has broken through a wall. Directly at the right is an aerial photo of the Arizona fissure cone.

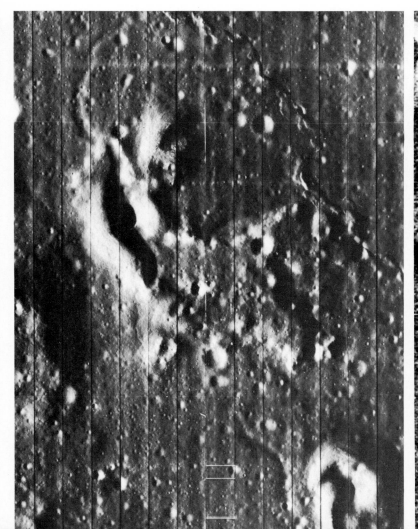 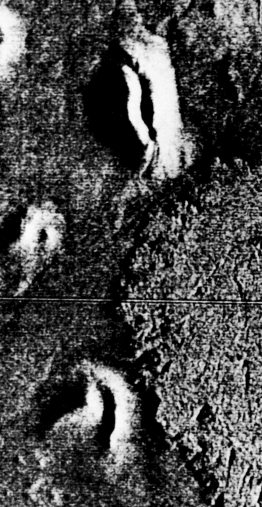

conclusion that Venus' rotation has somehow become Earth dominated. Understanding how this came about is a major intellectual challenge.

Scouting Earth/Moon

As the Centaurian explorers might have known that they would, from the time they first glimpsed the Earth and Moon from afar, they would surely close in for a reconnaissance of this seemingly "double" planet. They would quite logically scout both bodies at moderate distances, all sensors at work to seek a comprehensive understanding of the system. Their approach, in fact, might be like that of 15th-century ocean explorers working ship around a new Pacific isle, eying the land that had just come over the horizon, watching for a passage through the barrier reef and for easy sources of fresh water, seeking a suitable protective bay in which to career ship and refit.

Soon they would perceive that the double planet was a fairly small planet attended by an unusually large satellite. Their instruments would reveal the Moon to be an airless, waterless world, its axial rotation captured by its primary, its surface temperatures spanning the range from 240° F to —220° F, its tortured surface preserving the scars of uncounted past events. The planet Earth, in contrast, would seem a beautiful, bright-colored sphere. It would be partly veiled by whorls and streaks of white gases in its otherwise semitransparent atmosphere. The colors of the planet would be blue, white, brown, dark green, and russet red. Sometimes, excitingly, a unique bright-silver glitter would shine from the surface.

Two white polar caps could be seen (not at once), but it would be a challenge to the Centaurians to distinguish between the polar caps and the clouds. It should be easy to observe that the planet had a 24-hour rotation about axes tilted a bit more than 23° to the orbital plane; and equally easy for those as intelligent as the Centaurians to note that this arrangement not only provided in most latitudes a rich variety of seasons but also a felicitous broadening of temperate zones. Sensors would detect the planet's radiation belts and magnetic field; from the latter and from the Earth's high density —the highest in the solar system—the visitors might deduce that our planet probably has a liquid metallic core deep beneath its variegated surface.

Instrumental analysis would show that Earth's atmosphere is a combination of nitrogen and oxygen, lightly spiced with carbon dioxide, argon, and trace elements. It is thick enough to serve as a global heat-transfer mechanism and as a shield against lethal energetic particles and bits of rocky solar-system debris racing in at hypersonic velocities. But for all its complex and ever-changing white turbulence, the atmosphere would also be frequently semitransparent, giving the planet a window on the universe.

The Elixir of Life

Quite the most remarkable aspect of this blue-white planet—making allowance for the fact that one does not know what Centaurians are accustomed to—is the compound that covers more than two-thirds of the planetary surface. By spectroscope it is a hydrogen-oxygen compound with the property of being a solid below about 32° F, a liquid up to 212° F (at 14.7 psi), and a vapor or gas above. In its liquid phase the compound is extremely reflective, sending a Sun glitter back to Centaurian eyes and sensors that is perhaps unique in the solar system. And although the remote sensors might not indicate it, this compound—known on Earth as water—is both a kind of near-universal solvent and an elixir of life.

At this point it is easy to imagine the explorers vectoring their spacecraft in for a closer look at this planetary Eden of habitability. Rather than imagining their reactions henceforth, it may be better to quote Astronaut William A. Anders, who saw the planet under comparable circumstances:

The Earth looked so tiny in the heavens that there were times during the Apollo 8 mission when I had trouble finding it. If you can imagine yourself in a darkened room with only one clearly visible object, a small blue-green sphere about the size of a Christmas-tree ornament, then you can begin to grasp what the Earth looks like from space. I think that all of us subconsciously think that the Earth is flat or at least almost infinite. Let me assure you that, rather than a massive giant, it should be thought of as the fragile Christmas-tree ball which we should handle with considerable care.

AS11-36-5324

A majestic panorama of an entire hemisphere unfolds outside the windows of a spacecraft nearing or departing from the planet Earth. This view, though cropped by the window frame at the bottom and by the film's edge at right, shows the Northern Hemisphere all the way from the Pacific at left to the Mediterranean at right. The icecap delineating Greenland is a principal remnant of the last Ice Age, when similar glaciation extended over much of the land area shown in this photograph.

2
The Restless Atmosphere

*For we are dwelling in a hollow of the Earth and
fancy that we are on the surface.*—PLATO

WE SPEND OUR LIVES under an invisible, intangible blanket of more than 5 million billion tons of air, and could not survive a minute without it. Yet few of us pay much attention to this continually stirring, 20-mile-deep blanket in which the globe is wrapped unless it threatens our lives, property, or pleasures. Those extraterrestrial explorers of our solar system who were envisioned in the preceding chapter would surely be quick to recognize the beauty and examine the functions of the Earth's atmosphere.

It both shields our planet's crust from much of the Sun's radiation and is a gigantic component of the environment required by our form of life. The abundant water vapor in the atmosphere is heated mainly by solar radiation reflected from lands and seas, supplemented now by thermal radiation from myriad manmade sources, and is set in self-generated motion that is modified by the spin of the planet. Water vapor in this turbulent medium is condensed into cloud forms; moved often for great distances; precipitated as rain, hail, or snow; and replenished by surface evaporation, mostly from the sea.

The welcome precipitation, however, can quickly become a scourge when the moisture is mixed with certain combinations of temperature and pressure. Rampaging weather, according to a recent estimate, costs the United States alone at least 1200 lives and $11 billion in property in an average year.

Prolonged lack of precipitation, on the other hand, as in the tragic days of the Dust Bowl, can be as devastating as a temporary overabundance of it.

Weather's many moods affect all races of men, and in our reactions to it—ranging from terror or desperate thankfulness to mere irritation or a heightened sense of well-being—we are indeed a universal brotherhood. Most seriously concerned with the antics of weather, of course, are its professional forecasters and persons with especially large economic interests at stake: farmers, airlines, fuel distributors, power producers, clothing makers, resort proprietors, and many other groups. Their worries are shared by municipalities, which must contend with vexing transportation and cleanup problems. The weather affects everyone's taxes.

Now, moreover, President Nixon's Council on Environmental Quality has warned us that we may already have begun to change our weather—inadvertently—by our varied activities. Evidence continues to build up, the Council explained in its first annual report to Congress in 1970, that the scale, extent, and nature of human activities, and the rising population, may have begun to alter the chemical composition of the Earth's atmosphere and affect its heat balance. "And in turn these two alterations, in tandem," the report continued, "change weather and climate. But the processes and outcomes of such changes are largely unknown."

The photograph at the left is of a single big thunderstorm cell over South America. Its cloud shield was estimated to be spread over 60 miles of tropical jungle when an astronaut recorded it. Meteorologists found in this picture not only the storm's dimensions but, from the striking symmetry of its cloud shield, that it was practically at a standstill. If it had been moving, the shield would have stretched downwind in the anvil shape typical of thunderstorms in the temperate zones.

AS9-22-3374

AS9–19–3026   Like a thick, creamy soup coming to a boil, this extensive cloudiness over South American jungle land was erupting with several concurrent thunderstorms when photographed. The concentric cloud rings of the topmost cell, visible only from above, reveal the widening rims of successive central updrafts in the storm cell, which had failed to break through the tropopause and had spread out in all directions.

Hence knowledge of meteorological phenomena, and the ability to forecast weather accurately, have become even more vital to our generation than in 1870 when President Ulysses S. Grant signed the legislation establishing a national weather service, and placed the head of the Army Signal Corps in charge of it.

Meteorology was still a new science a century ago. But telegraphy had made possible warnings of what might be coming. Congress was prompted to establish a weather bureau by the loss of hundreds of lives in the 1860's to storms on the Great Lakes. Until then, Americans had relied mainly on folklore. Some but not all of this weather wisdom was based on thoughtful observations and was quite dependable. An example that found its way into children's books is the jingle that goes:

"Red sky at dawning, sailors take warning.
Red sky at night, sailor's delight."

18

Here the island of Hawaii looks like a dark-visaged monster peering up out of the sea beyond the lunar module in the foreground. The snow-tufted peaks of Mauna Loa and Mauna Kea resemble eyes, and the wedge-shaped cloud bank where the trade wind was flowing over the saddle between those peaks suggests a brow. There are often moisture-laden clouds on the windward side of a high tropical island and scarcely any on the leeward side.

AS9–21–3234

Modern meteorologists have found that this simple prognostication is reliable more than 70 percent of the time. Even arthritic elders who claim that they can feel an impending storm in their joints have been proven right too, in clinical experiments in which the falling atmospheric pressure and rising humidity of an approaching storm were simulated.

As men grew more sophisticated and their societies more weather sensitive, however, it became increasingly desirable to have more scientific means for foretelling weather conditions than jingles and aching ankles. Instead of wetting a finger and holding it up to note which way the wind was blowing, and tossing feathers into the air to find out how strong it was, men turned to the weather vane and wind gage. Then the thermometer, barometer, and hygrometer were developed. In time, it became evident that although it was useful to collect information on temperature, pressure, humidity, wind direction, and velocity at ground level in one's own immediate neighborhood, one must somehow extend this kind of investigation to the skies to gain adequate knowledge of what is brewing in the atmosphere. One of the first uses for balloons was to send instruments aloft to learn more about weather. The improvement in the accuracy of weather forecasting since then has been directly related to the scope and volume of meteorological data, the speed of transmitting it, and the swiftness with which it has been interpreted.

Weather's Four Prime Ingredients

The more men have learned about weather, the more fully they have realized how complex it is. A slight appreciation of its complexity can be gained from the meteorologists' estimates that 10 000 statistical varieties of weather are occurring at any given moment in the United States alone, and that throughout the world at least 45 000 thunderstorms may develop in an average period of 24 hours.

Basically, nevertheless, weather consists of four prime ingredients: temperature, pressure, humidity, and wind. The influences that manipulate them can be described, with drastic simplification, in a few sentences.

The Sun fuels the global engine that produces weather. The Earth, although intercepting only a two-billionth part of the Sun's total radiant energy, receives enough of it every minute to match an entire year's output of all of our manmade powerplants. Nearly half of this solar energy is lost to space, however, by being reflected from cloudtops, icefields, and snow. The rest is first absorbed and then reradiated as heat from the oceans—covering almost three-quarters of the planet—and from the land. Water vapor, predominantly in the lower 5 to 10 miles of the atmosphere, absorbs this heat, condenses to clouds, and churns the atmosphere with the energy born of heat transfer. The clouds are put in motion by this energy, and their circulation is manipulated by high-altitude, high-speed winds spawned by the Earth's spinning. Atmospheric motion is modified further by the uneven distribution of the heat radiated from land and water, and by the presence of mountain ranges, shores, plains, valleys, and other surface features.

The world's weather is bred chiefly over water in the equatorial regions, where the Sun's radiant energy strikes most directly. There is more water

vapor in the atmosphere over equatorial seas and jungles than anywhere else on the globe. Updrafts of warm, moisture-saturated air rise from the tropics and flow generally toward the poles, where heavy, cold air from those regions sinks and spreads, generally toward the Equator. This circulation is far from neat and orderly, however, because both the friction of air passing over the rough and varied Earth and the rotation of the planet interfere with it in a multitude of ways. Over all the areas between the Equator and the poles, masses of air at varying temperatures and pressures intersect and interreact, gently or violently, producing benign, blue-gold days, restorative rain, blazing calm and drought, or the fury of great, whirling storms.

Some parts of the Earth's atmosphere do, indeed, behave with dependable regularity. Out of the general flow of warm tropical air toward the poles, two currents, one on each side of the Equator—in what meteorologists usually refer to as the intertropical convergence zone—descend near the latitude of 25° and head back toward the region from which they sprang. Because of the spin of the planet, their homeward routes are not straight but diagonal. These are the steady, persistent trade winds, which have long been of great importance to us. The trade winds carried the first seamen to new shores and still are heeded by navigators of ocean-going vessels.

The collection of meteorological data from the equatorial and polar regions always has been sparse because of the difficulty of travel and settlement there. Even now, a decade after the first weather satellite was placed in orbit, less is known meteorologically about those vital weather-producing areas than about the other parts of the world that they affect.

In the nearly airless region above the lower 20 miles of the Earth's atmosphere, other, more exotic influences are at work affecting weather in ways that are not yet fully understood. These influences include ozone layers, solar X-rays and ultraviolet rays, meteoric dust, magnetic storms, and drastic, mysterious temperature fluctuations. Why, for example, as radiosondes first discovered, is the high atmosphere near the poles subject to sudden winter warmings of as much as 50° or 60°, and why, at the same time, does the temperature above the tropics turn cooler? Why, conversely, when the

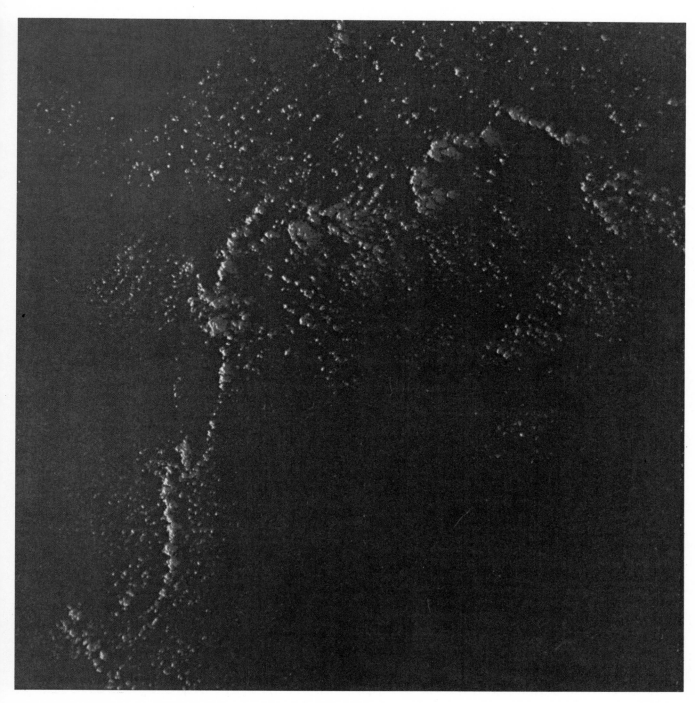

The delicate-pink filigree of tropical clouds at sunset in the photo above was recorded over the south Indian Ocean, east of Madagascar, by the automatic camera aboard unmanned Apollo 6. The southern expanses of the Indian Ocean have not been criss-crossed by trade routes the way that northern portions of that sea have been, and satellite pictures have revealed details that were unknown about meteorological phenomena there.

AS6-2-1075

21

AS6-2-1425

This picture of a typical formation of stratocumulus clouds over the Pacific Ocean especially interested meteorologists because of the sharp line from the top down toward the bottom near the center. To the left of that line, the clouds are tightly clustered; to the right of it, they are much more scattered, perhaps delineating the edge of a cold current or an area of upwelling over which the atmosphere tends to be more stable than it is above warm water. This photographic evidence was obtained off northwestern Mexico by the camera on Apollo 6.

AS9–21–3309

Cirrus clouds are the highest normally seen. Even when dry, high-pressure weather prevails on the ground; there is often enough moisture thousands of feet overhead to form these ice-crystal clouds. This wind-lashed procession of them was seen crossing the border from Mexico to lower Texas, and may have marked the swift passage of a subtropical jetstream that began southeast of Hawaii, swept up over Baja California, and sped on across Mexico. Near Del Rio, Tex., Amistad (Friendship) Dam and Devil's Lake Dam were backing up waters (in the lower right) of the Rio Grande, Pecos, and Devils Rivers.

tropical atmosphere is warmer than usual, does the atmosphere near the winter pole grow colder? Some mechanism is functioning that meteorologists are still trying to identify.

Mathematical Weather Prediction

In 1904, Vilheim Bjerknes of the Norwegian Geophysical Institute published a paper on "Weather Prediction as a Problem in Mechanics and Physics." He suggested that forecasting could become an exact science if measurements of temperature, humidity, pressure, and wind velocity at as many points as possible on the Earth's surface and in the air above it could be collected regularly and displayed in the form of a map that would portray the state of the atmosphere over a specific geographical area at the time the readings were made. The data would then be utilized in mathematical formulas to compute future weather conditions.

The Bjerknes theory was basically sound, but data gathering was primitive then, and the mathematical techniques needed to employ the concept were not yet adequate. The latter deficiency was remedied in essence, but not in practice, by a British mathematician, Lewis Fry Richardson, in 1922. His solution, explained in a treatise entitled "Weather Prediction by Numerical Process," appeared to face two insuperable impediments before it could be practically applied. Weather prediction by numerical process would require, Richardson estimated, surface and upper-air data from more than 2000 permanent weather stations strategically located around the world. If that volume and variety of data were obtainable, which seemed a remote possibility indeed in 1922, it would demand the full-time calculations of 64 000 mathematicians every day of the year to reduce the data to the requisite formulas for forecasting weather.

Forecasters consequently had to go on making do with inadequate data and incomplete equations. Radio greatly speeded up the collection and dissemination of weather information, however, and the invention of automatic radio transmitters made it possible to add a host of robot reporters to the information-gathering network of human observers. The robots not only could be left in remote places to function by themselves but also could be sent aloft attached to small balloons carrying packages of meteorological instruments.

Radiosonde balloons are still the major source of detailed weather information for local operational forecasts. They rise through thousands of feet of atmosphere, continuously transmitting readings of the temperature, pressure, and humidity, until they burst and are automatically parachuted to Earth. Ground-based radars track their progress and obtain the essential measurements that they are unable to supply themselves—upper-air wind directions and velocities. Few radiosondes are launched from ships, however, and there are still vast areas of land over which radiosondes do not travel on their relatively short flights.

Even so, by the end of World War II, the volume of meteorological data being obtained from the radio observers was threatening to overwhelm the forecasters. Taking note of their plight, the late John von Neumann of Princeton's Institute of Advanced Study began work with a group of meteorologists to develop a special computer and a technique for utilizing it to analyze weather information and produce forecasts. "The hydrodynamics of meteorology," he found, "presents without doubt the most complicated series of interrelated problems not only that we know of but that we can imagine."

The von Neumann computer, capable of doing the work of 100 000 mathematicians, proved to be surprisingly accurate in predicting weather on its first trial in 1950, but it was unable to maintain that initial level of performance. Like all computers, it was no more reliable than its programing, and the equations that were fed into it obviously needed further refinement.

The use of high-speed electronic computers to store, collate, and analyze meteorological data and make operational weather forecasts became routine by 1956, marking one of the greatest single advances in the history of meteorology. Current forecasts are more than 85 percent reliable; 2-day forecasts are more accurate than 1-day forecasts were 10 years ago; but beyond 72 hours, weather predictions tend to stray farther and farther from reality. Efforts to improve both the computers and the equations given to them to solve are, of course, continuing.

The machines used routinely now for Weather Bureau forecasts are many times faster than von Neumann's pioneering computer. They can per-

The camera aboard unmanned Apollo 6 captured this spectacular view of long cirrus clouds with transverse bands over the Atlantic, about 100 miles northwest of Dakar on the westernmost tip of Africa. These clouds probably marked the location of a subtropical jetstream that starts a bit east of the tropical region of the Atlantic and sweeps up over the Sahara to the southern Mediterranean. Research meteorologists think the transverse bands may indicate a spiraling circulation within the jetstream.

AS6–2–931

26

form a billion computations a second. But it has become clear that even more data, from many more locations around the globe, must be obtained before the computer equations can produce forecasts reliable for more than 3 days in advance. Ironically, if data of that volume and comprehensiveness were obtainable right now, current computers would be unable to cope.

Research meteorologists say that computers a hundred times faster than today's fastest machines will be needed, as well as much more complete data than are now available, to make accurate 2-week weather forecasts possible. Such computers are being developed, and the volume and scope of raw weather data are constantly increasing.

In 1966 a study panel of the National Academy of Sciences concluded that reliable 2-week forecasts are within the competence of present technology. Another study sponsored by the same prestigious organization estimated that in the United States alone the dollar benefits from such long-range forecasts would be at least $2.5 billion a year in four major sectors of human activity: agriculture, flood and storm control, transportation, and construction. It is easy enough to think of other areas where the gain would be great: recreation, for one.

The Meteorological Satellite's Advent

Man's daily information about the world's weather began to increase by several orders of magnitude in April 1960 when NASA placed the first meteorological satellite, Tiros 1, in orbit about 450 miles above the Earth. This gyroscopically spin-stabilized satellite, circling the globe once every hour and 30 minutes, carried two small television cameras. The panoramic views of Earth's cloud patterns that these cameras telemetered to receiving stations created a sensation among meteorologists. Never before had men been able to observe the formation and movements of clouds on a synoptic basis from hundreds of miles above, over huge expanses not only of populated territory but of portions of the surface, such as the oceans,

Hurricane Gladys (at left) was stalled west of Naples, Fla., when photographed from Apollo 7 on October 17, 1968. Its spiraling cumuliform-cloud bands sprawled over hundreds of square miles. A vigorous updraft hid the eye of the storm by flattening the cloudtops against the cold, stable air of the tropopause (then at 54 000 feet) and forming a pancake of cirrostratus 10 to 12 miles wide. Maximum winds near the center were then 65 knots.

AS7-7-1877

AS7-8-1919

On October 19, Gladys (the hurricane shown on the facing page) was photographed again from Apollo 7. By then it had moved across Florida, generated top winds of 85 to 90 knots, and its eye was near Jacksonville. It sped on, crossed Cape Hatteras on October 20, and reached Nova Scotia the following day as an "extratropical low."

Meanwhile, on October 20, the Apollo 7 camera was photographing Typhoon Gloria (below) 480 miles south of Kyushu, Japan. Its eye was then about 50 miles wide, and looked especially malevolent because a small twist of cirrus seemed to be serving as a kind of pupil, and violent winds rimmed the eye with a wall of clouds.

AS7-8-1930

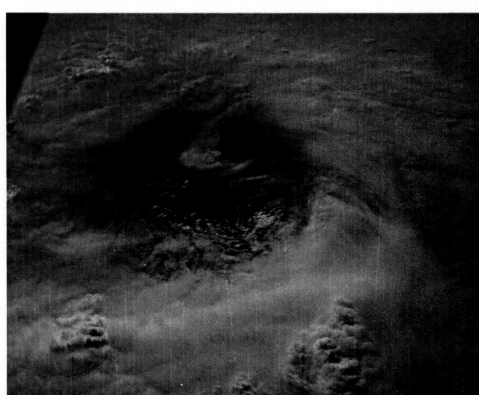

AS9-23-3592

An aging, faltering storm, this low-pressure area about 1000 miles north of Hawaii was 3 or 4 days old and beginning to break up when it was photographed from a spacecraft. The extensive cirrus cloud shield that ordinarily covers vigorous young storms had disappeared, and the typical spiral pattern of the lower clouds was very clearly revealed. A research meteorologist looking at this picture said, "This is now just a swirling puddle of air, moving slowly across the Pacific."

AS9-22-3415

From above southeastern Georgia's estuary-threaded coast, an astronaut photographed the passage of a cold front down the Florida peninsula. Behind it, cooler, more stable air moving in from the north had cleared the sky over north-central Florida and revealed a part of the Gulf of Mexico (at the right). Well-defined cloud streets extending out over the Atlantic indicated a steady wind from the northwest with abundant moisture at the lower levels. Near the horizon a thunderstorm towered south of the tip of Florida.

AS6-2-973

A strong sea breeze was cooling Africa's west coast enough to prevent cloud formation for 20 to 30 miles inland when this picture was taken from over the Gulf of Guinea. Some 30 to 40 miles offshore, meanwhile, air sinking to replace the air moving inland was evidently creating a vertical circular pattern, causing a conversion and forming a distinctive cloud line parallel to the shore. Wisps of cirrus in the clear area were thousands of feet above the surface and not affected by the sea breeze crossing the shores of Ghana, Togo, Dahomey, and Nigeria.

Here you see white clouds building up on the windward side of mountains and gray smoke from fires burning along the Pacific coast of Mexico. Some plumes of smoke are long and slim, oriented in the direction of the prevailing breeze. This denotes stable air in which pollution is liable to persist. Other plumes are breaking up and widening downwind quite rapidly, indicating atmospheric turbulence in which smoke pollution will not linger long. Over a plateau inland the plumes indicate that the wind there was northerly to northeasterly.

31

AS9-23-3617

Orbiting astronauts often saw a cloud eddy off the ancient Moroccan seaport of Agadir and the west coasts of Morocco and Spanish Ifni. Sometimes the spiral was tight, sometimes open, as above, depending on the windspeed. An eddy is formed whenever the prevailing northeasterly wind is strong enough and there is sufficient moisture in the local atmosphere to produce clouds. The wind sweeps down past Cape Rhir, where the coast cuts abruptly eastward. The swifter air currents are on the seaward side and the slower ones inside.

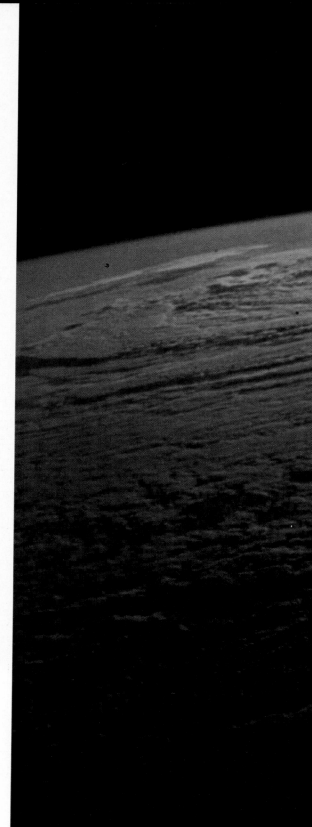

The photograph at the right of a distant, dying storm over the sea west of Australia was taken by an Apollo 11 astronaut on the way to the first landing on the Moon. The clouds in this vast panorama look as if they had been smoothed off by a trowel. There is not a thunderstorm in sight. (A five-sided light spot was produced within the camera.) Such a broken stratus formation is typical over the fairly cool waters west of Australia, as it is over the Pacific a couple of hundred miles west of California.

AS11-36-5295

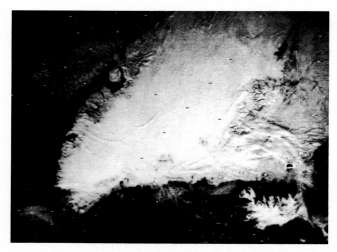

Greenland and Antarctica support 96 percent of all the glacial ice left on Earth from the last Great Ice Age. Nimbus 3's TV camera took this picture of Greenland's thousands of square miles of ice, more than 7000 feet thick in some places, on a day when there were virtually no clouds in the sky over it.

icefields, and deserts, from which little or no meteorological information had previously been obtainable.

Manned satellites flew in orbits within about 30° of the Equator in the 1960's and the astronauts photographed cloud formations there from lower altitudes than Tiros 1. The color pictures that they obtained with hand-held cameras helped meteorologists interpret the views televised in black and white from the unmanned spacecraft, and at the same time gave the layman a better idea of the immensity and complexity of the phenomena that the meteorologists were struggling to understand.

Even the early Tiros pictures revealed spirals typical of hurricanes and typhoons in progress, and it immediately became apparent that visual imagery from satellites would be of significant importance in a warning service to advise people of the birth and probable course of the world's most dangerous storms. This service was begun by a cooperative arrangement between NASA and the Weather Bureau, but the latter assumed full responsibility when it took over a Tiros satellite for operational forecasting in July 1965. The following February, the Weather Bureau became part of a much more comprehensive organization, the Environmental Science Services Administration (ESSA).

Since then ESSA satellites have kept a close watch on every major storm that has threatened

any part of the United States. They also have tracked all the principal storms detected in the Atlantic and Pacific Oceans. ESSA 5 made meteorological history in September 1967 by concurrently tracking a total of eight storms in both oceans. In 1969, weather satellites detected and followed the courses of 22 hurricanes and 17 typhoons.

NASA and ESSA continue to cooperate. The space agency develops vehicles and instruments with the advice of ESSA, and provides the launching facilities and orbital checkouts for the latter's operational series.

Once weather satellites were incorporated into the daily system of national weather forecasting, cloud analyses (called nephanalyses) were regularly sent to local forecasters by facsimile transmission, along with conventional weather maps. The views from space are also obtainable upon command at hundreds of ground stations in 50 countries. An Automatic Picture Transmission (APT) system now installed on operational satellites has made this possible. Cloud analyses based on satellite TV imagery are handed to pilots of transoceanic airlines before takeoff. They also appear nightly on many commercial TV weather programs, with the cloud patterns overlaid by drawings of the geographical areas affected.

More than a million satellite cloud pictures have been received since 1960, and they have given the meteorologists a better three-dimensional concept of the skies than was formerly obtainable. (A group of black-and-white pictures in this chapter shows how a colossal 1969 storm was followed.)

Highly significant, too, are the weather data obtained by special instruments, especially the high- and medium-resolution radiometers and spectrometers carried by experimental satellites. (A second set of black-and-white pictures in this chapter illustrates the transmissions from Nimbus 4.) In a single day, the infrared spectrometer on Nimbus 3 has provided as much information as 10 000 radiosondes or sounding rockets could have yielded.

With data now streaming down in torrents, researchers can reconstruct a vertical temperature profile of the atmosphere from top to bottom over nearly any part of the Earth twice a day. They also are beginning to get comparable information about water vapor on a global scale by correlating pictures of cloud distribution with data from other sensing devices. Accumulated and analyzed by a computer, satellite-acquired information can describe the heat budget of the whole atmosphere, detailing how the energy of the Sun is being utilized to generate weather and where its many varieties are being bred. This has been hailed as a further significant advance in weather forecasting.

The ability of satellites to make vertical temperature soundings reduces the need for radiosondes and sounding rockets, but data will still be needed from balloons sailing at constant altitudes, oceanographic buoys, and ground-based radars, including lasers that see farther and probe the water-vapor content of clouds more precisely than conventional radars.

Future weather satellites may carry radars into orbit and perhaps be equipped with small computers for preliminary processing of the data they acquire. It has also been suggested that eventually a system of satellites making coordinated observations of the environment above the atmosphere may be needed, and their findings integrated with those of satellites probing the atmosphere, to complete men's knowledge of the Earth's weather.

The largest, most complex, and most versatile of NASA's experimental weather satellites now is Nimbus 4. It weighs 1366 pounds and was launched into a polar, Sun-synchronous orbit on April 8, 1970. Its "high noon" orbit keeps the Sun directly behind the spacecraft, and thus provides good lighting for pictures of all sunlit parts of the Earth that its TV camera takes at local noon each day. Nimbus 4 is also equipped to take pictures at local midnight

AS9–23–3501

A luminous line of clouds lit by the setting Sun crowned the shore of western Australia when the photographer pointed his camera south to record that continent's appearance through an early evening haze. In the foreground, you can see a thunderstorm cell, beyond which an old cold front from the Indian Ocean was continuing to push away the clouds that marked its arrival. Darkness was descending on the desert expanses to the left of the bright clouds, although some areas of high reflectance still gleamed palely.

35

daily; these images are obtained with an advanced infrared radiometer in the process of measuring the Earth's absorption of solar energy and its thermal radiation.

The more jobs that satellites can do simultaneously, the less expensive they become as a means of gathering information. In addition to probing the atmosphere from outside, Nimbus 4 relays data collected hundreds of miles below and transmitted to it by robot ground stations, oceanographic buoys, and balloons.

The World Weather Watch Program

Even the most technologically advanced nation cannot achieve perfection in weather forecasting by itself because the world's atmosphere is indivisible. A meteorological event in one portion of it is certain to influence other portions. Recognizing this, the World Meteorological Organization and the International Council of Scientific Unions have combined efforts in an intensive, 10-year program called World Weather Watch. Its goal is to find out what

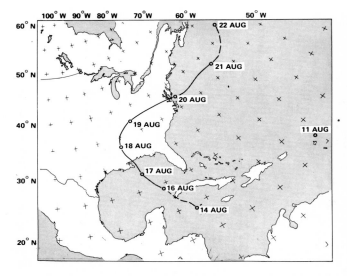

Camille was the fiercest tropical storm ever recorded in the United States. Satellite discovery and tracking of this hurricane saved possibly 50 000 lives; about 75 000 persons were evacuated from its path before it struck near Biloxi, Miss. The map shows the sinuous course traced by the center of this storm from the Gulf to the Atlantic.

AUG. 11, 1969: Camille began to take shape in the Caribbean —but was not yet a true hurricane.

Camille's winds and the tidal wave that struck near Biloxi, Miss., left havoc such as this.

AUG. 19, 1969: The lessening storm poured torrential rains on the land as it moved north.

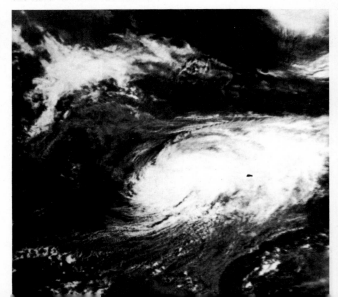

meteorological knowledge we still lack to understand the mechanism of weather well enough to make reliable long-range forecasts, and to determine and perfect the instruments and techniques still required to control weather judiciously.

The most massive World Weather Watch experiment to date was conducted from May through July 1969 in the eastern Caribbean, a notorious breeding place for hurricanes. There, for the first time, an international team with highly sophisticated tools made an intensive study of the interactions of sea and air. Their inquiry ranged from 18 000 feet below the ocean surface to 100 000 feet above it. This BOMEX (Barbados Oceanographic and Meteorological Experiment) involved hundreds of people, two dozen airplanes, 10 ships, a dozen oceanographic buoys, and seven weather satellites. The objective was to learn comprehensively what went on in this particular incubator of weather, so that the knowledge could be applied to all other regions where sea meets air. Such knowledge, it was hoped, would enable forecasters to move closer to

AUG. 16, 1969: Camille whirled into the Gulf of Mexico and was seen approaching the north shore.

AUG. 17, 1969: Its winds reached 190 to 200 mph, and brought a 25-foot tidal wave with the storm.

AUG. 20, 1969: Camille lost its spiral shape entirely as it passed over Chesapeake Bay.

AUG. 21, 1969: Camille faded, but another hurricane, Debbie (below), developed behind it.

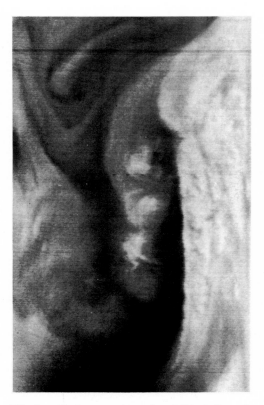

Nimbus 4's temperature-humidity infrared radiometer provided this vertical view of jetstreams cutting deep furrows through lofty clouds over central Europe at midnight. Dark streaks from top to bottom show the jetstream.

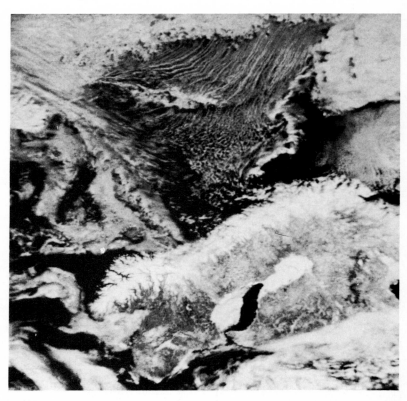

Nimbus 4's TV system transmitted this picture of Scandinavia (in foreground). Across the top you see the ragged edge of pack ice, and a fringe of clouds descending from a storm system in the Barents Sea. Note how much more reflective the snow on Norway's bald mountains was than the snow in Sweden's forests. A tongue of open water is visible in the Gulf of Bothnia.

achieving a mathematical model by which weather could be predicted with more accuracy and for longer periods.

World Weather Watch plans to follow up this experiment with a broader one in the South Pacific. This one will have field headquarters at Kwajalein, in the Marshall Islands, and last 18 months, beginning in 1972. It is intended to cover an expanse of tropical ocean and islands 2000 miles long and 1000 miles wide. One of its goals will be to determine how best to obtain meteorological observations around the world in order to achieve dependable 2- to 3-week global forecasts. World Weather Watch expects to climax its work in 1976 with a global meteorological experiment, linking every technologically advanced nation in a massive study using all of the Earth's outdoors as a laboratory.

If, as many meteorologists confidently expect, a time comes when highly reliable long-range forecasts can be made routinely, the computers then in service should be able to predict what would happen if any of the known ingredients of weather were deliberately altered. Scientists are sharply divided on the question whether large-scale modification of the weather is desirable—some foresee immense benefits, and others fear ecological disaster.

Small-scale efforts to modify weather—by cloud seeding, to increase rain and decrease hail and snow, and fog seeding, to clear airports and superhighways—have often been successful and beneficial, but not consistently so. Large-scale efforts, such as Project Stormfury, to seed the centers of young hurricanes for the purpose of literally taking the heat out of them before they can become full grown, have not yet been conclusive. Hurricane seeding provided enough promise to encourage the Govern-

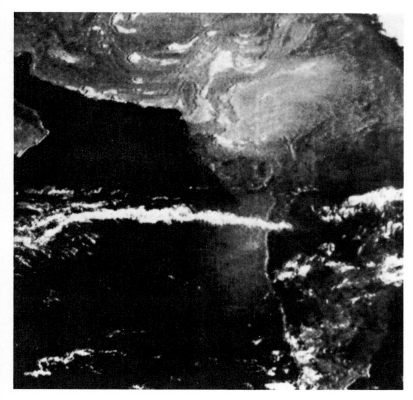

India was baked in sunlight and largely free of clouds when Nimbus 4 passed over it from south to north at an altitude of about 700 miles on April 9, 1970. In addition to the reflectivity of land, sea, and clouds that this picture reveals, it shows a large area of sun glint on the Indian Ocean just off the west-central coast of the subcontinent of Asia.

India's coast is sharply defined here by differences in thermal radiation from the warm land and the open sea. This infrared-radiometer image obtained at midnight was sharper than a TV picture taken at noon.

ment to announce that Project Hurricane would seed storms "massively and repeatedly" in 1970. To play safe, however, this hurricane seeding was limited to storms that appeared unlikely to move within 50 miles of populated areas.

"Worldwide ground monitoring of turbidity, carbon dioxide content, and water vapor distribution in the atmosphere should be done with particular attention to oceanic areas," the Council on Environmental Quality believes. "Satellite monitoring of global cloud cover, atmospheric heat balance, and surface albedo should be accelerated. Research on models of the thermal and dynamical processes with the atmosphere and the boundary between the atmosphere and the solid Earth and oceans needs emphasis."

AS7-7-1741

Oahu is in the lower center of this photo of the blue Pacific Ocean. Honolulu is on the near shore. Volcanoes raised the 1600-mile-long chain of Hawaiian islands along a rift in the sea floor in the Cretaceous period of geologic history. Men navigating canoes by the stars found these bits of land much later. The eight main islands and many coral-fringed islets now constitute our Nation's oceanic State.

40

3
The Waters of Earth

Time and the ocean, and some fostering star,
In high cabal have made us what we are.
—SIR WILLIAM WATSON

UNTIL ABOUT SIX CENTURIES AGO, sailors were reluctant to venture out on more than a tenth of the Earth's waters. As the great navigators of the 15th century set sail, emboldened by better ships and a spirit of conquest, they were profoundly ignorant of the great oceans they probed, unaware that the Atlantic was broadly S-shaped, or that beyond the New World was a still larger, nearly round new ocean. We know more about other planets today as we begin to probe them than our predecessors knew about the far shores they were to find. In one respect alone—the duration of voyages of exploration—we show ourselves more conservative. We plan space travel in terms of weeks, whereas the Dutch successfully colonized the East Indies with a sailing technology requiring 4 years for a round trip.

Life on Earth is believed to have originated in the oceans, growing from small molecules of amino acids and nucleotides. The small molecules collided in water, and linked themselves together to form large molecules of proteins, DNA and RNA, from which living organisms developed. Thus the multibillion-year course of evolution began.

Water was the medium for changes in other compounds that made our existence possible. It is an almost universal solvent. This accounts for the presence of most of the known chemical elements in sea water. Although some of them have not been detected yet, all of them are thought to be there.

"All of the basic elements of living things on Earth could be spread out in a thick paste on the Moon, and yet they could never unite to form the simplest living molecule," the Director of the Goddard Institute for Space Studies, Robert Jastrow, has observed, "because they would be unable to move about and collide on its dry surface."

As a solid and as a gas, as well as in liquid form, water also serves us in wonderful ways. It expands when it freezes. Ice floats, and this has been of enormous consequence to us. If ice did not float, quiet bodies of water would freeze from the bottom up, destroying the aquatic life in them. If sea ice sank, it would expose the Arctic and Antarctic waters to the Sun's radiant energy. Those waters would be greatly warmed, glacial ice would melt, and the sea level would rise enough to drown many of our large coastal cities.

Along with this catastrophe would come such a rise in the Earth's average mean temperature that many now inhabited parts of the world would become intolerably hot. The planet's climate would undergo almost unimaginable changes. If, on the other hand, the heat balance of the planet were to tip the other way and ice were to spread from both polar regions as far as the 45th parallel (it once reached as far as the 50th) in both the northern and southern hemispheres, all the rest of the water on Earth would freeze, and this would soon be a frozen world.

In gaseous form, as water vapor, this extraordinary compound travels through our atmosphere to produce the rain and snow that keep the Earth from becoming like the Moon.

Geologists believe that oceans and dry land have coexisted on Earth, in one ratio or another, since

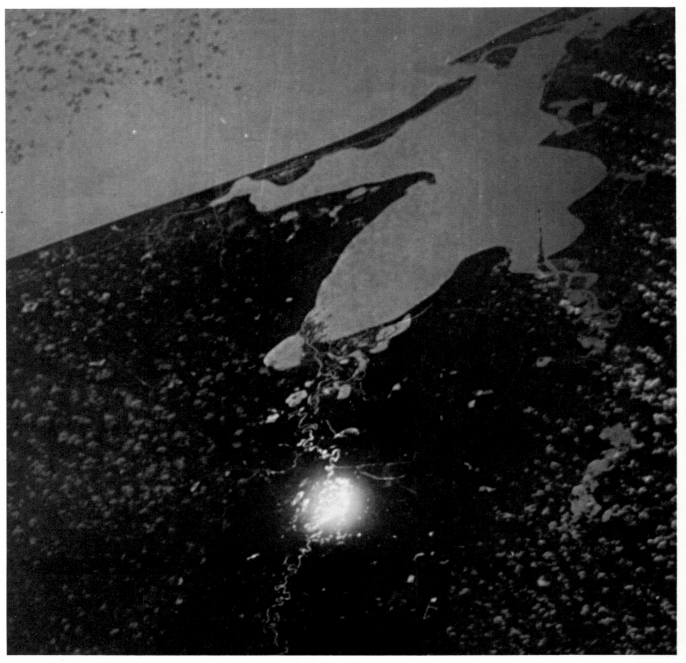

AS7-7-1787

The Earth's waters have determined sites and sizes of our cities. Although this looks like a night photo, it was taken in morning light while Apollo 7 was crossing Texas. The view is to the east, toward the rising Sun, and that bright spot is the reflection of the Sun from the Trinity River, which flows into Galveston Bay north of Houston. Although details of the land are not visible, the Houston Ship Channel, dredged through Galveston Bay, stands out as a dark line of tailings.

42

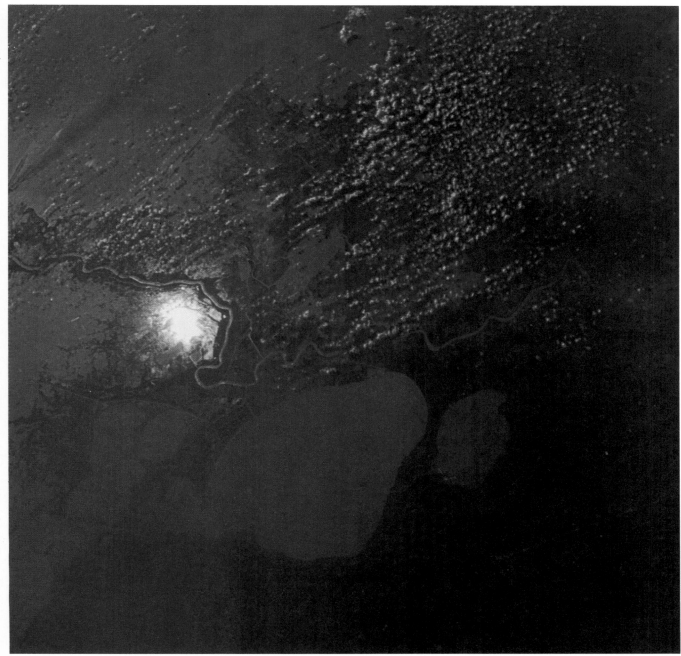

AS7-7-1789

One minute after taking the preceding picture of Houston, the Apollo 7 astronauts saw the Sun's reflection from the myriad swamps and lagoons south of the Mississippi River and New Orleans, one of our country's most romantic ports. Lake Pontchartrain is in the foreground and the lines above it are drainage canals. The Mississippi River delta extends into the Gulf of Mexico at the upper left. Hurricane Camille (pictured in the preceding chapter) forced thousands of people to evacuate this area in 1969.

AS7–5–1632

The Sun's reflection reveals a variety of surface conditions in satellite pictures. This southerly view of the Gulf of California from over Mexico shows where the water was smoothest and the wind lightest. When the brightest point of sun glint moves into a flat, calm area, dark patches briefly become silvery white. Surface conditions account for the dark plume visible off the shore of San Pedro Nolasco island.

early in the planet's history. The total volume of water on Earth—the seas are estimated to contain 350 million cubic miles of it—has remained remarkably constant through the ages, according to the well-known modern British geophysicist, Sir Edward Bullard. No one knows, however, quite how the equilibrium has been so neatly maintained. The level of the oceans has varied, to be sure, but water has never covered all of the land or even most of it. The oceans were at their lowest levels during glacial periods when much of the planet's water was locked in thousands of miles of ice.

Evidence of the work of water has been found in the Earth's oldest rocks. It is thought to have been released from condensing clouds and the cooling crust during the first billion years of Earth's existence. When the rains first came, they are believed to have poured "unceasingly for centuries."

Without oceans, scientists have pointed out, there would be no extensive precipitation, and consequently the lands would lack salt-free ground water. Many billions of tons of water evaporate from the ocean surfaces every day, leaving their salt content behind. The water vapor forms clouds, which carry it elsewhere, releasing some over the seas, some over the land. Eventually, most of the precipitation that falls on land finds its way back to the seas, largely by way of Earth's many rivers. Bearing salts from the soils and rocks in solution, the rivers add— although at an infinitesimally slow pace—to the sea water's average salinity. This is still only a little more than 3 percent of the volume after millions of millennia. The oceans would be much more salty if myriads of creatures and plants living in it did not absorb the salts for purposes of their own.

The atmosphere drives the great currents in the oceans. The currents, in turn, help determine the amount of heat that the oceans release to the atmosphere, and where it is released, and thus have profound impact on our weather conditions. The global circulation of water also has significant economic effects. In places where there is upwelling of colder water from the ocean depths, for example, nutrients are brought to the surface, creating the world's best fishing grounds.

The Bible refers poetically to mariners as "those who plow the paths of the seas." Their need for harbors and anchorages have determined the locations of many great cities. The oceans have both

AS7-7-1779

The Sun blazed on Socotra Island and the Indian Ocean for this photo. Left of the sun glint, between the big island and smaller ones called The Brothers, a slicklike eddy is darkly outlined. Note the fine, white, horizontal line below Socotra. Waves rolling over an undersea shelf 10 miles offshore may have produced it.

isolated and brought human races together, and the shorelines have been changing ever since cartographers began to trace them. Waves and currents have straightened the shores in some places, filled harbors with sand in others, and built up sand spits, hooks, and barrier beaches on the continental shelves.

Oceanographers remind us that the oceans still undoubtedly conceal a multitude of wonders. A fifth of our oil and natural gas now comes from undersea wells, and greater reserves remain to be discovered beneath the waters. We have barely begun to explore the mineral wealth there. Three chemicals— sodium chloride, magnesium, and bromine—are being extracted commercially now from sea water, and various quantities of other useful compounds are dissolved in it.

One aspect of underocean wealth—manganese nodules lying on the bottom—has staggering dimen-

45

sions. The origin of these potato-shaped lumps of ore, which contain valuable amounts of copper, cobalt, and nickel as well as manganese, is still uncertain. They appear to accrete, in the course of millions of years, around some small object the way that a pearl is formed.

Most of the high-grade manganese nodules located by survey ships are at depths ranging from 5 000 to 15 000 feet, posing major problems of retrieval. One study estimates that the Pacific Ocean alone contains more than 350 billion tons of them, enough to last 400 000 years at the present rate of consumption. An American and a West German firm have recently joined forces in an effort to gather nodules from the Atlantic floor by using a huge underwater vacuum cleaner operating from a ship in water 3000 feet deep.

Water may also provide energy for future generations of men in a way not even foreseen until our century. If the hydrogen-fusion process for releasing energy is tamed, each gallon of water will theoretically have the energy equivalent of 300 gallons of gasoline.

When improved technology makes the conversion of salt water into fresh water feasible on a large scale, a burgeoning world population need no longer fear a shortage of water suitable for drinking. Sea water is being desalinated now for use in the sheikdom of Kuwait and on the Caribbean island of Aruba. One American city, Key West, and the U.S. Navy Base at Guantanamo rely principally on sea water.

It is no wonder that thoughtful men stand on a shore facing the open sea with a tingle of exhilaration as well as a feeling of solemnity and awe.

The Importance of Sun Glint

The obvious first use for spacecraft that could ascend above the atmosphere was to observe the atmosphere. The ocean surface mirrors the sky, and the seas look blue because of the ways in which light is absorbed and reflected. Hence it should not have surprised us when scientists at the National Environmental Satellite Center in Suitland, Md.—after study of data obtained from hundreds of miles in space—found that they could be useful to oceanographers as well as to meteorologists.

High-resolution infrared radiometers aboard the Nimbus weather satellites have enabled specialists to develop charts of sea-surface temperatures, needed to increase knowledge of ocean circulation and the location and movement of its currents. Scientists have also found that images of the Sun's reflection on the surface of water can be interpreted to provide readings of surface windspeeds. This clearly is a matter of interest, not only to meteorologists but also to the shipping and fishing industries, since it may delineate the present or immediately pending state of the sea.

The study of sun-glint patterns on water as indicators of surface windspeeds has revealed the seemingly paradoxical fact that pictures taken from great distances can be more informative than pictures taken from low altitudes. The area of sun glint visible in pictures taken from ATS–1, riding 22 300 miles above the Equator in mid-Pacific, and from ATS–3, in a comparable position over the Atlantic, is much more extensive than it is in pictures obtained from satellites orbiting closer to the Earth.

The ATS cameras provide a resolution—about 2 nautical miles—as good as that of the cameras on the near-polar-orbiting, Sun-synchronous ESSA satellites only about 700 miles above the Earth. ATS–1 and ATS–3 are in geosynchronous orbits, effectively hovering in a fixed position while the sun glint moves from east to west across the tropical waters far below them. This makes their pictures, delivered every 20 minutes, a more comprehensive source of this special kind of information than any other satellite pictures.

Researchers have established a scale of interpretive values for the sun-glint pictures that enables them to determine sea states ranging from flat calm to the degree of roughness generated by a 30-knot wind. The scale is based on the relative size and brightness and texture of the solar reflection on the sea. When more sophisticated instruments, such as microwave radiometers and laser altimeters, can be placed on satellites, scientists confidently expect to develop a broader range of sea-state observations from space. The microwave radiometer should provide a significant degree of cloud penetration, and be helpful in monitoring the mood of the sea in the most heavily traveled shipping lanes.

Clouds often make it difficult to extract oceanographic information from satellite images of the Earth. Someone has said, resorting to the language of electronic communication, that clouds are the

AS7-4-1590

From over the South Pacific, not far from Tahiti, one sees little but water, clouds, and some delicate blue-green rings that look like cakes of clear ice. They are coral atolls of the Tuamotu Archipelago, with surf ebbing and flowing over their low, slender rims. Coral polyps built up such atolls, sometimes in shallow seas, and sometimes around volcano rims that later sank out of sight. They are products of geologic and biologic processes that have continued over long periods.

47

AS9-22-3432

This view of the Cape Verde Islands is "a fluid dynamicist's delight." Each cloud streak in the center was caused by an island interrupting the northeast trade winds. (Some were produced by islands outside the picture at the right.) In the distance, semicircular cloud lines alternately turn in different directions. This is a classic demonstration of the Von Kármán vortex, an interweaving of oppositely curving wind currents after passage around an island.

AS9-22-3429

This is a nearly vertical view of two of the Cape Verde Islands. The waves evident in the sun glint beyond Sao Tiago, the upper island here, are believed to have originated far below the surface of the sea when the prevailing current met the island. The crests of such internal waves are sometimes several miles apart. The whitish region in the lee of Sao Tiago indicates a calm region of upwelling. Both the wind and sea current turn right to flow around these islands (south of the Equator they would turn to the left).

AS9-22-3345

A deep gorge follows a dogleg course through shallows around some of the Bahama Islands. Here you see the dark-blue tip of the Tongue of the Ocean clearly defined against coral sand. Off Andros Island (in the upper left) shoal water is only from 35 to 40 feet deep, but in the nearby tongue the sea is 4400 feet deep. Some oceanographers believe the ridges in the sand around the tongue here indicate that a deep countercurrent is entering it to curve westward around Andros. Farther north, this strange gorge in the Atlantic is 10 000 feet deep.

50

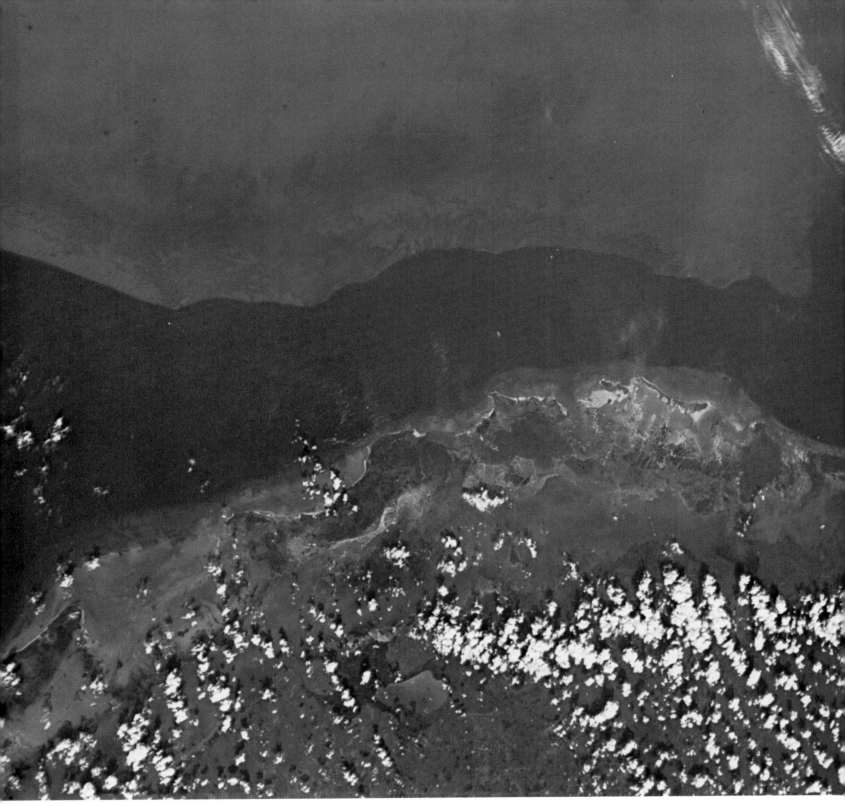

AS9-22-3343

Features below the ocean's surface have been discerned in many satellite photos. In this one the Old Bahama Channel reveals its deep-blue gorge north of central Cuba. It is 1500 feet deep at the northwest end (left) and 3700 feet deep at the southeast end. Steep escarpments forming the channel walls show clearly. Coral keys of the Archipelago de Camagüey fringe the southern wall of the channel here. The slightly darker areas in the clear blue sea on the far side of the channel in this view are areas in which there is vegetation in the shoal waters.

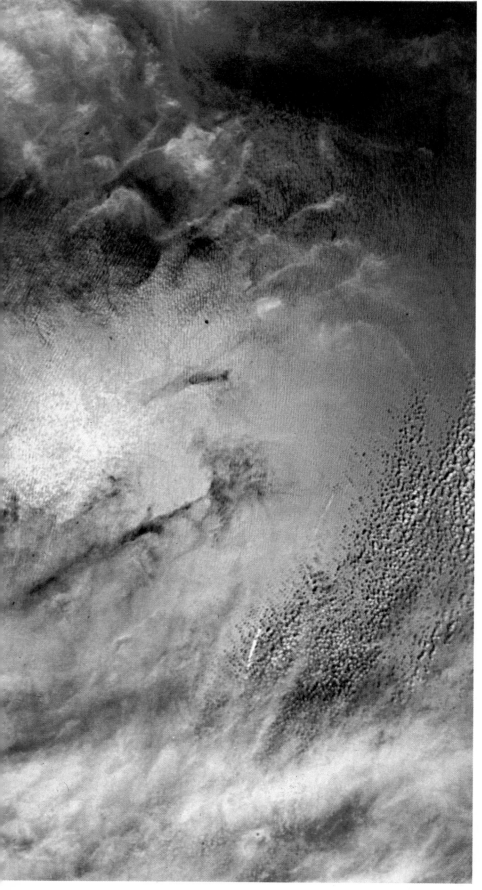

meteorologist's signals, the sources of his information, whereas to all other scientists trying to derive specific knowledge from viewing Earth from space, clouds are "noise," garbling the message.

Clouds are sometimes distinct clues, nevertheless, to what is happening on the ocean surface or in the midst of an icefield. Breaks in clouds, for instance, over portions of an ocean known to be generally warm sometimes reveal that in those clear patches the surface water is colder than the surrounding waters. Air flowing over cold water tends to be more stable than air flowing over warm water, and thus clouds are less likely to form over cold spots. Conversely, an opening through an icefield permits heat to pour out—almost an outgassing—from the warmer water beneath the ice. This generates characteristic clouds, which inform the trained observer that there is a break in the ice below those clouds.

The National Environmental Satellite Center has developed computer techniques for deriving representative sea-surface temperatures from areas where clouds are scattered; in effect, selecting and analyzing readings from the areas of open sea and eliminating those contaminated by clouds. ESSA researchers have also devised an interesting technique for routinely producing large-scale pictorial charts of ice and snow boundaries. These charts have been especially helpful in the United States and Canada. (Four of ESSA's composite minimum brightness charts, at the end of this chapter, show how spring came to the northland in 1970.)

Although picture maps of ice and snow help the meteorologist determine the heat balance of the Earth and its atmosphere, they are even more valuable to the hydrologist. An important part of the world's supply of fresh water is temporarily stored each year in snow cover. It is the hydrologist's job to predict how much will eventually become available in liquid form for man's uses. The hydrologist is also expected to predict floods, when snow and meteorological conditions warn of the likelihood of them. Shipping interests depend on him to foretell the buildup and breakup of ice in lakes and rivers.

In January 1969, satellite pictures enabled the Weather Bureau to issue early warnings of record floods that swept down later that spring through the Midwest from the Canadian border. Study of the pictures spurred aircraft and ground observers to check and find out that the threat implied in the satellite pictures was indeed serious. Computerized

The sun glint shows a well-defined swell pattern in this photo of the Atlantic off Morocco. An advancing swell line in the upper left is diagonal to swells below it here, a clear indication of a shoal where the swell line pivots like a gate. The average distance between swell crests disclosed the sea's state to oceanographers studying this picture.

AS9-23-3617

flood predictions based on the accumulated data set in motion Operation Foresight, which made Federal disaster aid available for the first time *before* predicted floods arrived.

Satellite pictures that enable the hydrologist to keep track of where the snow lies on huge areas of the Earth's surface, coupled with satellite instrument readings that tell him the surface temperatures on a twice-daily basis, make possible much more precise and timely predictions of runoff.

The satellite pictures of ice conditions on oceans and large lakes and bays have been especially useful to shippers, but the resolution of the ESSA vidicon system has not been sufficiently high to yield meaningful observations of ice in rivers. Hydrologists of the National Environmental Satellite Center anticipate that with the introduction of infrared radiometers of higher resolution than those currently in use on ESSA satellites, it will not only be possible for them to obtain more precise information on lake and river ice conditions but also to survey sea ice at high latitudes during the long polar night.

Oceanographers and hydrologists both foresee advances in their disciplines when Earth Resources Technology Satellites go into orbit later in this decade. The resolution of the TV imagery from those satellites will be many times better than that now obtainable from weather satellites.

NASA scientists have studied the Earth's waters both to insure the safety of astronauts descending on them and to increase all men's knowledge of the seas. A large group spent 10 days in the summer of 1970 examining one of the strangest anomalies below the surface. Utilizing the heavily instrumented tracking ship that is normally part of the two-way communications network linking the Manned Spacecraft Center at Houston with astronauts on Moon missions, these men electronically traced the contours of the deepest gorge in the Atlantic floor, the Puerto Rican trench. Beneath this 5-mile-deep trough lies a mysterious mass so dense that it deflects the pull of gravity, causes the ocean surface to dip a measurable amount, and throws navigators off course by falsifying the readings of their instruments. As a result of this study, the scientists expect to be able to improve instruments for mapping the world's oceans.

"The sea has always challenged the minds of man," Rachel Carson wrote, "and even today it remains the last great frontier of Earth."

Between Brunswick and Savannah, Ga., the downslope of the continent's edge and sediment carried into the Atlantic by rivers are visible from space. In an opening in the clouds at the upper right edge, a V-shaped notch marks the ancient mouth of a drowned river valley. Slim dark streaks in the sun glint below it are jet contrails' shadows.

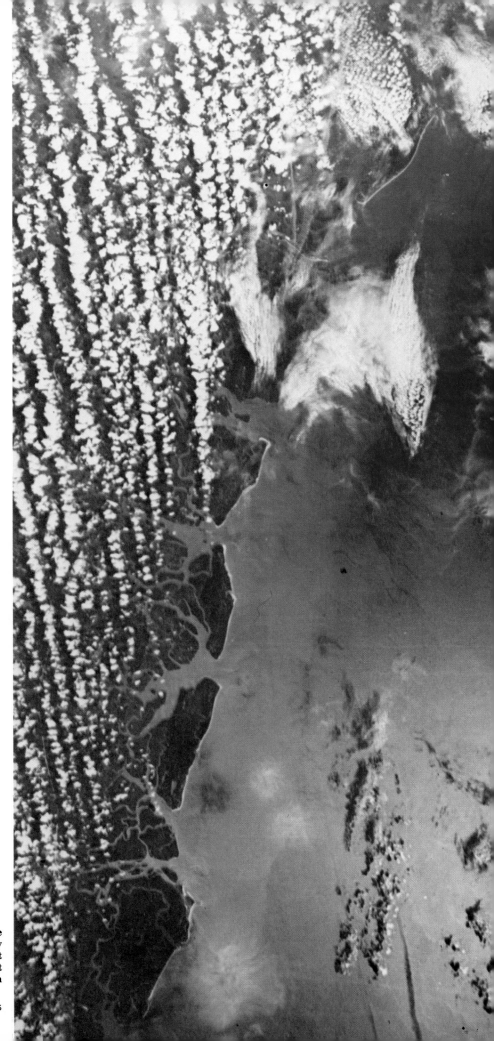

AS9-26A-3727A

The color infrared photo (above) of the Texas coast near Galveston shows the direction in which sediment, streaming off the land in a pale-blue fringe, was being carried by a steady southwesterly current in the Gulf of Mexico.

54

At the right, in a photo of Schouten Island, great breakers thundering shoreward from a typhoon gave this island off the coast of New Guinea a white edging. Left of that surf, the sun glint reveals swirling eddies full of sediment. Leeward of the main island, a long plume is sediment being borne away by the ocean currents.

AS7-4-1607

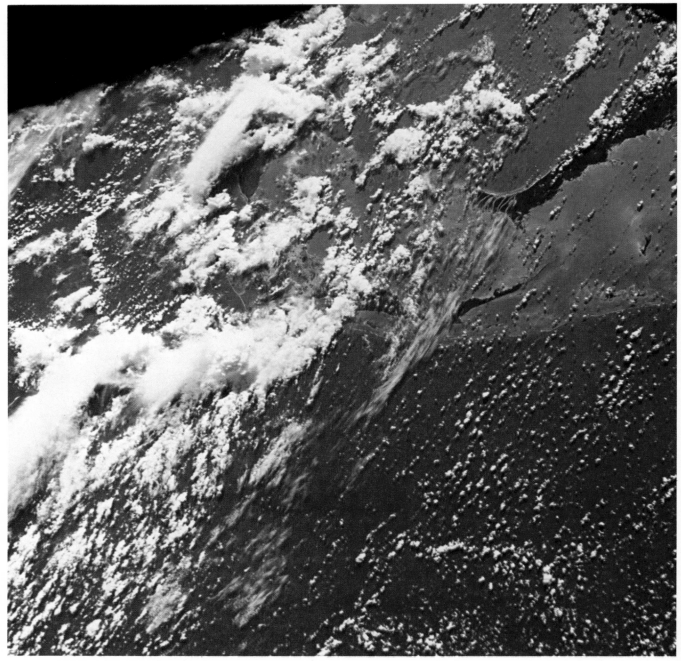

AS7–11–2040

The paleness of the ocean's color around the Grand Bahama (upper right) and Great Abaco Islands in this photo, taken from the north, shows the shallowness of the water near their shores. The enveloping Atlantic is about 3 miles deep where it appears cobalt blue in the foreground, but shoals fringe these islands. Oceanographers would like to have such pictures of the Bahama islands after every major storm, because they might indicate what undersea barriers the storm had broken through and which ones had been re-formed by it.

Jamaica feels the steady influence of northeast trade winds. In this photo, taken with the camera pointed nearly vertically, both the cloud lines and the swell patterns in the sun glint confirm the persistent set of the winds. Kingston is on the first bay from the right on the lower shore here, and Montego Bay is the notch at upper left.

AS9–21–3316

The frieze below is a cluster of the Lesser Sunda Islands (Alor, Pantar, and Lomblen) east of Java. There is scarcely any pale-blue fringe around them because they rise steeply from great depths. Such depths surround volcanically active islands in many parts of the world, and especially in Indonesia.

AS7–4–1612

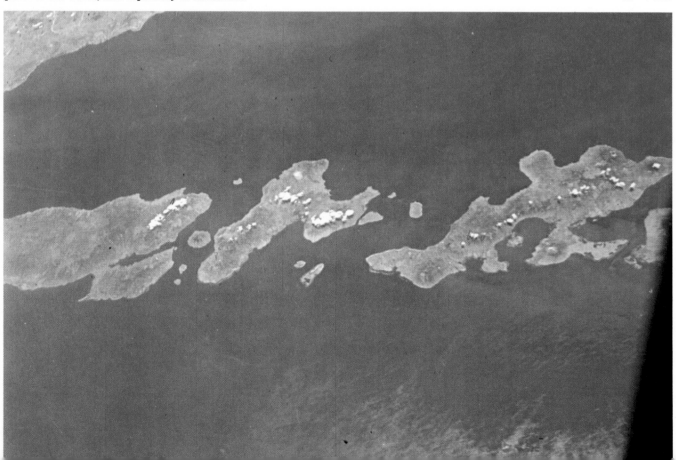

You are looking south here at the upper Gulf of California. Sun glint and a slender pattern of cumulus clouds, shaped rather like a question mark, help define a small area of high pressure over it. The dark patch in the center of the Gulf is calm water, in the eye of an anticyclonic circulation produced by a breeze blowing up the Gulf over a cooler surface than the flanking land. The white, snakelike figure near the shore in the center is the salt-encrusted bed of a dry stream.

AS7-4-1740

The Hawaiian Islands are farther from the nearest continent than any other islands in the seas. Niihau, the farthest west of the main group, is in the foreground here. A Hawaiian king sold Niihau in the 1800's for $10,000 to private investors, who made it into a single ranch not open to the public. The clouds to the right of it here are over the Kaulakahi Channel between Niihau and a much larger island, Kauai. Beyond Niihau there are many tinier islands in the vast Pacific.

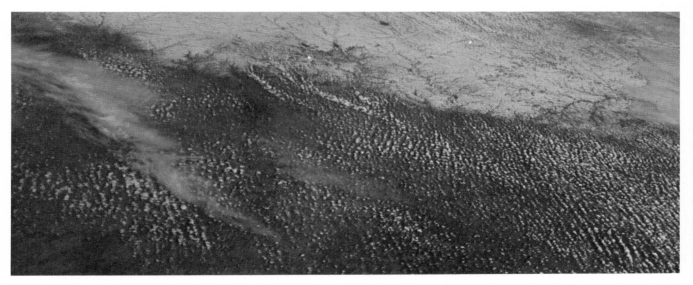

AS9–23–3483   Both pictures on this page were taken on the same day, March 8, 1969. In the view above, from over Arkansas, it was easy to distinguish the southern edge of a snow blanket over the Midwest from the cumulus clouds starting to form over warmer land. But this was a rare atmospheric condition. Clouds and snow often look alike from space.

AS9–22–3327   In this photo, broken clouds over mountains in Arizona and New Mexico were hard to distinguish from snow. A new technique, illustrated on the next page, now facilitates ice-and-snow surveys from spacecraft by reducing this difficulty. This technique can help forecast floods and safeguard shipping in the future.

60

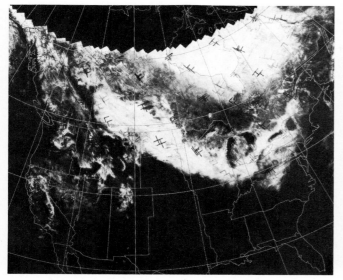

FEB. 9—13, 1970: A 5-day composite minimum brightness chart produced by ESSA showed snow cover on North America. Dark bands across Canada were forested areas, where snow cover was partly masked by conifer branches.

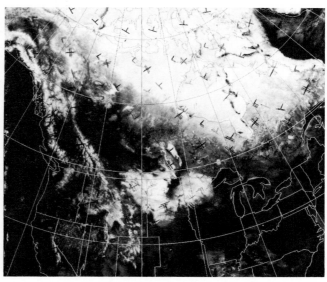

APR. 15—19, 1970: A similar chart showed the snow retreating from the Great Lakes area, effects of a spring blizzard west of them, and passages for summertime shipping beginning to open in the ice of Hudson Bay.

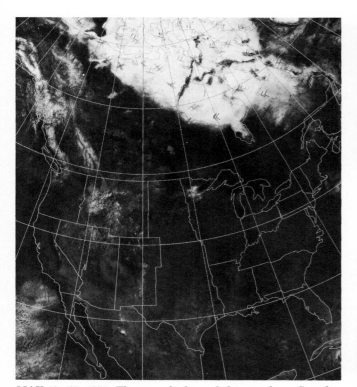

MAY 19—23, 1970: The snow had receded to northern Canada and western mountain ranges. Persistent cloudiness accounted for the pallid overlay on the sea off Baja California.

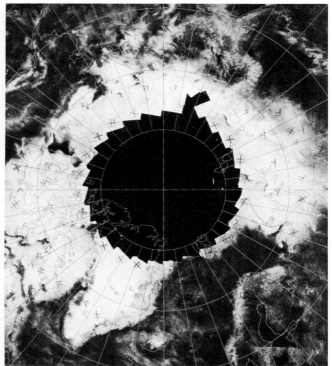

By the end of May, this polar composite showed, snow remained on Greenland, northern Canada, and Siberia. The water around Alaska, upper left, was now open.

AS7–7–1748

The Earth's highest peak is Mount Everest, only 29 028 feet above sea level. It is near the S-shaped lake in this oblique westward view of the Himalayan Range between Nepal and China. Many other peaks here are nearly as high. The Ganges River at the left is on India's side of the range, and the lakes at the right are on the Tibetan Plateau. Edmund Hillary's expedition in 1953 was the first recorded human ascent to the summit of Mount Everest.

4
The Lands of Earth

*We do not realize what we have on Earth
until we leave it.*—JAMES M. LOVELL

FORTUNATELY FOR US, the Earth has a rough surface. If it were as smooth as, say, an ideal ball bearing, it would be covered by water nearly a mile and a half deep. From the distance of the Moon, the masses of land above sea level resemble mere figures on a child's ball, but from shorter distances the mountains, hills, and plains of the continents can be seen and relations between them become apparent. The photographs in this chapter were taken from Apollo spacecraft orbiting our globe before the first landings on the Moon.

To a strange creature flying by the Earth for the first time after inspecting the Moon, the continents might seem less intriguing than the restless atmosphere and the huge, glinting oceans. To most men, however, the variety of terrain in color and structure is especially fascinating. Most of our knowledge of the Earth has been obtained by nearsighted study of minute details of its crust, and its protuberances and depressions have restricted both our mobility and our perspective.

For the last two centuries geologists have proceeded on the assumption that the same processes that are underway now also operated before anyone was here to observe them. This hypothesis and the data collected by field study are the bases of their theories about the Earth's origin, development, and structure. But if, as scientists agree, the present is a key both to the past and to the probable future of our planet, it is a complex key. Many parts of it still are only dimly perceived, and have been measured only approximately. Hence the model of

the Earth in the minds of geologists is neither precise nor complete.

Change is the essence of the Earth's story as well as that of every living thing on it. Vast structural movements have many times raised—and wind, rain, and lava flows have repeatedly erased—features of the Earth. Mountains lifted above water have been scoured at times by mile-thick ice. Much dry land was once sunk beneath the sea, layered in places with hundreds of feet of sand, silt, and shells turned to stone.

The solid crust of the Earth is now believed to be only about 30 miles deep. This thin skin floats on a mantle of highly compressed rock that is about 1800 miles thick and so hot that it is almost fluid. Beneath it, for more than 2000 miles, there is inferred to be a core of iron, perhaps entirely molten, perhaps molten in its upper regions but solid at the center.

From fossil-bearing rocks, geologists have deciphered with considerable detail the story of the Earth's last half-billion years. At that point the fossil record begins to fade, although recent evidence suggests that microfossils occur in rocks formed 3.5 billion years ago. No rock of earthly origin has been found to be older than 3.5 billion years. Yet many meteorites are much older, often 4.5 billion years. There is now wide agreement among scientists that this is the approximate age of the solar system. What, then, became of the evidence of the Earth's first billion years? The planet's own structural contortions and weather's obliterating influences seem to have completely erased it from the continents.

One might expect some clues to the Earth's infancy to have remained in the floors of the oceans, protected as they are from forces to which areas above sea level are exposed. The oldest rocks found there, however, have turned out to be relatively young. None has been judged to have been formed more than 150 million years ago, and many of the core samples extracted have been found to be only about half that old. The rocks from the floor of the sea, moreover, are mainly igneous—the sort created by congealing lava flows.

How does one account for this? Sir Edward Bullard and many other contemporary geophysicists believe that the ocean floor is being continually renewed by molten basalt from the Earth's interior. The new material oozes up, they think, through a crack between two ridges of a mountain chain that winds for 40 000 miles through all of the great oceans. As this molten matter solidifies, it thrusts the huge platters that support our continents farther apart. Some parts of the ocean floor are believed to be widening 6 inches annually. At that rate, new sections of ocean floor as extensive as that of the 10 000-mile-wide Pacific could be laid down in a mere 100 million years. Scientists who accept this plate-tectonics theory hope that further investigation of it will lead to an understanding of the earthquake belts that have been traced in mountains both below the sea and on the continents.

The Earth's face ages so gradually that many changes in it are hard to measure. Nevertheless, to scientists such as Robert Jastrow of the Goddard Institute for Space Studies, "large pieces of the Earth's crust appear to be moving about like cakes of ice in a bathtub."

The eastern Pacific floor, for example, seems now to be heading toward South America and plunging under that continent at an angle of 45°. There its basalts may be remelted as they sink into the hot mantle below the Earth's crust, to be spewed out of volcanoes in the Andes.

Evidence has been found that South America has been drifting farther west from Africa for the last 70 million years. Obviously, if South America's eastern coast and Africa's western coast were edges of jigsaw-puzzle pieces, they would fit together rather nicely. There is evidence, too, that the Arabian Peninsula between Africa and Asia has been pulling farther away from Africa for 20 million years, widening the Red Sea and the Gulf of Aden as if nature were intent on producing a large ocean there.

In photographs of the Earth from orbiting spacecraft, both adherents to the theory of continental drift and the skeptics have found evidence in support of their views. The pace at which the continents may be changing positions may be determined better in the near future by using beams from lasers on Earth and reflectors on the Moon to keep a constant check on the distances between landmarks on separate continents.

By landing on the Moon, setting up instruments there, thumping it, recording its vibrations, and bringing back lunar material for analysis, men are learning now how greatly the Earth differs from it. The new knowledge of our planet that has accrued as a result of the space program prompted Prof. Frank Press, who heads the Department of Earth and Planetary Sciences at the Massachusetts Institute of Technology, to remark, "We have already learned more about the Earth by going to the Moon than we have by any other experiment performed on Earth." One of the rocks brought back from the second landing on the Moon appeared when first tested to be 4.5 billion years old—a billion years more ancient than any of the Earth's native rocks.

Textbooks used by today's geology students still contain such statements as: "In spite of the impressive lists of data being assembled about mountains, no theory proposed for the cause of mountain-building has been generally accepted." Data now becoming available may clarify, modify, or confirm scientists' concepts of the Earth's past and future. "The hum of mighty workings" becomes clearer even to casual viewers of space photography.

The High Places

The roughness of our planet's surface and experiments on it have led some researchers to believe that the Earth has expanded like a balloon, shifting and tilting masses of solid matter to produce mountains and valleys. Others have compared the folds in the mountains to the wrinkles on the skin of a dried apple, and have ascribed such irregularities to shrinkage of the Earth's face as it has aged.

Augusto Gansser, a noted Swiss student of mountains, reported a few years ago that upward move-

64

AS9-25-3685

Popocatepétl, one of Mexico's most famous volcanoes, is the snow-capped peak nearest to the lower right edge here. It is 17 848 feet high. Its close neighbor, Ixtacihuatl, rises 17 347 feet. Cerro La Malinche in the center is a lower, more isolated volcano. You can see the crater at its summit. Notice, too, the smoke plumes. Vegetation is sometimes burned to clear land on the mountain sides. Most of Mexico's people live on rugged tableland, such as this area near Puebla.

ments were still active in the Himalayas, and attributed much of their present altitudes to geologically recent events. B. Sahni, another student of such matters, ventured the further suggestion that it may have been easier to cross the Himalayas thousands of years ago, when the first human migrations began, than it is now.

Throughout recorded history, however, the Himalayas have been a more formidable rampart between central Asia and the Indian Peninsula than all the sweat and toil of China's millions of men could build for their emperors on their kingdom's northern frontier. Baber, Emperor of India and First of the Great Moguls (a kinsman of Tamer-

laine and Genghis Khan), led his troops across the Himalayas, and found the cold so biting that some men (whom he knew by name) lost their hands and others their feet. Scaling the Himalayan peaks is still one of the most arduous challenges to adventurers.

Even lesser mountains have both inspired and frightened men for many more centuries than scientists have studied their structure. The Japanese have long considered their little islands' highest point, Fujiyama, "the Supreme Altar of the Sun," and every year thousands of pilgrims ascend it to signify their reverence for ancient gods. Gautama Buddha found his enlightenment in the mountains

65

AS9-23-3511

From an astronaut's vantage point, one can gaze down into the tremendously deep chasms of the Hindu Kush range in the Himalayas. The sky above the white crowns of snow on the peaks was clear when this photo was taken, but clouds filled the valleys. Temperatures as well as altitudes vary widely in this part of the world. When the morning Sun warms the highlands, fierce cold winds rush down the mountain sides to increase the rigors that men must endure to climb them.

AS9-20-3173

At dawn, the high points of the Himalayas reflect the Sun's light while the chasms are still dark. Two peaks at left center catch the light before the neighboring terrain. The average elevation of the Tibetan Plateau is about as high as the most towering Rocky Mountain peaks between Canada and Mexico. This range has isolated the Indian Peninsula from the rest of Asia both geographically and culturally for as many centuries as men have written history.

67

AS7-5-1667

In Afghanistan, west of the Himalayas, between Iran, Pakistan, and the Soviet Union, the Koh-i-Baba Mountains rise nearly 17 000 feet. The elliptical, light-colored features seen here are large igneous intrusions. The *Encyclopaedia Britannica* says that in these mountains the volcanic action prior to the upheaval of recent strata and the folding of highlands is "evidenced by occasional mud-boiling volcanoes." The river shown here is the Panjshir, a tributary of the Kabul system.

AS7-6-1697

The southern half of the Sinai Peninsula is in the foreground, and the Red Sea extends to the horizon here. The camera was pointed south, so the Gulf of Aqaba is at the left and the Gulf of Suez at the right. In addition to the intermittent drainage pattern and the historic mountains and deserts visible in this space photo, specialists have pointed out that it shows coral growth in the Strait of Tiran between the Red Sea and the Gulf of Suez. The Earth hereabouts has many intriguing features, some of which are shown on the next two pages.

Three of the great rift systems found in the Earth's crust meet in "the Afar Triangle." This part of Ethiopia and the Somali Republic is thought to be a continuation of the Red Sea's emerging floor. Linear ridges seen here are fault scarps. Black patches are lava flows and the white areas are salt lakes.

This is a vertical view of the southern part of the Afar Triangle. Scientists knew little about this hot, desolate area until 1967 when an international team began a detailed study of its towering escarpments, fissures, volcanoes, and below-sea-level deserts. It is near the Red Sea's junction with the Gulf of Aden.

Moses learned God's laws on one of the Sinai Peninsula's mountains. The large photo here shows all of those mountains, and also those on the far sides of the Gulfs of Suez and Aqaba. The Red Sea is in the foreground, and the Mediterranean's eastern end is below the clouds on the horizon. The Earth's crust here is both rugged and complex.

AS9-23-3514

Men believed for many centuries that the horizon you see in this photograph taken from a spacecraft was the edge of the world, and dared not sail too close to it. The western end of the Mediterranean Sea is in the foreground, and the Strait of Gibraltar between it and the Atlantic Ocean is in the center of this picture. Africa is at the left and Europe is at the right. Much of civilization's history was written by the navigators and explorers who ventured forth from these blue waters. Note how clearly the complex folded mountains of Morocco and Spain can be seen to have affected the patterns of high winds and cumulus and cirrus clouds.

72

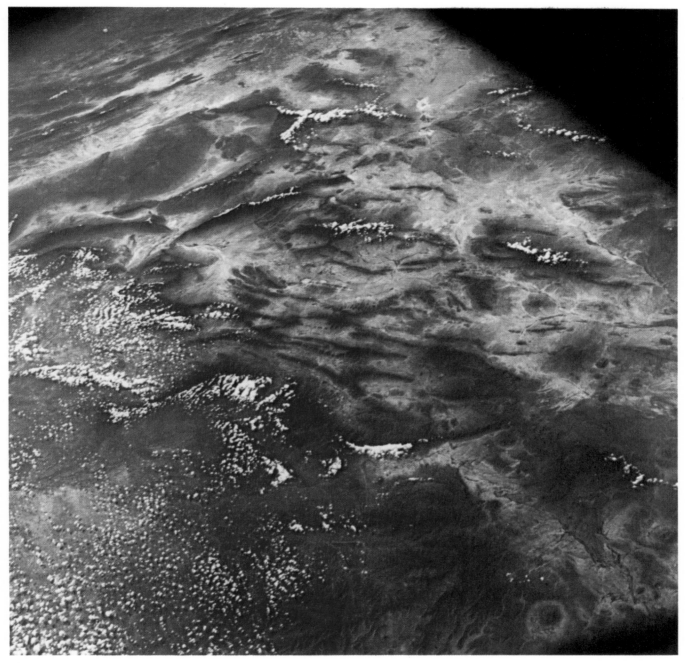

AS7–6–1732

Here you look down on the New World, to which European explorers' curiosity, faith, love of adventure, and yearnings for riches led them in the 1500's. This view is to the south from over northern Mexico. The cumulus clouds follow the Sierra Madre Oriental, an immense, folded mountain chain that consists of sedimentary rocks that were deformed and uplifted toward the end of the Cretaceous period. Near the top of the picture, the farms in a broad valley around the city of Torreón are visible. The circular feature at the lower right is in the Burro Mountains, and is probably a Tertiary igneous intrusion that has been exposed by erosion.

73

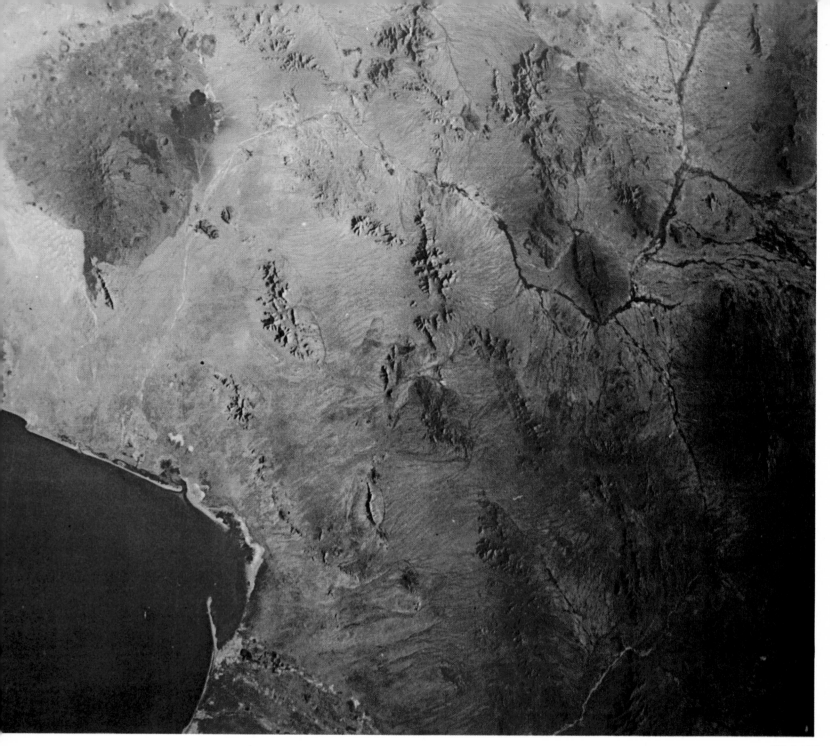

AS6-2-1438

The Pinacate volcanic field of Mexico is in the upper left of this space photograph. The Bahia de San Jorge at the northeastern end of the Gulf of California is in the lower left. The Organ Pipe Cactus National Monument, north of the boundary between Mexico and the United States is in the upper part of the picture. The river near the volcanic field is the Sonora. (More space pictures of the mountains to the north of this western part of North America will be found in ch. 6.)

74

AS9-26A-3780A

This is a color infrared picture of the Sierra de Juarez at the northern end of Baja California. It is an area inscribed with lines of geological significance. Cape Colnett is at the lower left, where the shoreline resembles the profile of a face. Snow still covered parts of the mountain range in March when this photo was taken. The mountainous spine of the peninsula extends south from here to the Tropic of Cancer. Parts of the coastal land are cultivated, but the flora and fauna that throve before men occupied this region have been disturbed less than in other parts of the continent.

75

This line of clouds was built up along the crest of the Sierra Madre Occidental Range near the Pacific shore of Mexico and Guatemala. Canyons that look so deep in an oblique photograph give indication of how high these mountains must seem when viewed from the farmland in the foreground.

The bleak wall seen here is on the Pacific coast of South America, at Antofagasta in northern Chile. There are salt flats in the depressions between these complex sedimentary hills and mountains; the large one is the Salar de Atacama. This view extends across Chile to part of Argentina.

That little white cone in the clouds near the right center edge is Fujiyama. Some 12 500 feet high, it can be seen on a clear day from 13 of Japan's provinces. The large bay between the clouds is Ise Wan, the approach to Nagoya, and this view extends across the Sea of Japan to Asia. Fujiyama last erupted in 1706.

of Nepal; the Greeks believed their Gods dwelt on Olympus, and Moses conversed with Jehovah on Mount Sinai. "Faith!" Walt Whitman wrote after crossing the Alleghenies in a stagecoach at night. "If I had an infidel to convert, I would take him on the mountains of a clear and beautiful night, when the stars are shining."

For many centuries, nevertheless, most migrants went around rather than over mountains, if they could. Friar Lopez de Gomara, who accompanied Hernando Cortez into Mexico in the 16th century, reported that there—

> *the simple Indians thought . . . Popocapec, which is to say a hill of smoake, . . . was an infernall place, where all such as governed not well, or used tyrannie in their offices, were punished when they died, and also believed that after their purgation they passed into glory.*

Now space photography can help armchair travelers as well as explorers appreciate the majesty of distant mountains. It is also aiding laboratory scientists as well as hardy climbers in studies of the mysteries of the origin and formation of mountains. Only from space can one see how defiantly the Himalayas tower over the Earth's largest continent, what a perfect dome the snow on Fujiyama appears to be in the white clouds, and how emphatically the Andes of South America and the Western Cordillera of North America block the winds from the Pacific.

Men have been trying to remold the continents to gratify their needs and whims for only a small fraction of the Earth's lifetime. The processes that have produced and reduced mountains will continue to limit our management of our environment, and some of those processes can best be observed, like the figures in a huge mural, from a respectful distance.

Even in well-surveyed parts of the world such as the United States, space pictures have shown many faults, some active, more accurately than they had been mapped by field geologists. In all parts of the world, an engineer can better foresee the regional effects of a proposed reservoir or any other large structure, if pictures of vast areas, taken at different times of the year, can be placed side by side on his drafting table.

The Dry Places

Although bulldozers have nicked the Earth's face here and there, winds still whip around more tons of sand in its deserts. Elsewhere the rivers are still leveling the continents night and day and building deltas that dwarf the changes wrought in shorelines by engineers. "The Earth is uniquely favored among the planets: it has rain, rivers, and seas," Sir Edward Bullard once wrote, but some 14 million square miles of its landmasses get less than 10 inches of that rain a year, and another 14 million square miles get only from 10 to 20 inches.

Prospectors following riverbeds up mountains to look for gold and other metals have sometimes discovered both deserts and green valleys on the far sides of ranges. Every continent has desert areas, and they tend to follow the Tropic of Cancer and the Tropic of Capricorn around the world. About a fourth of the globe's exposed land, in fact, looks dry and hot from space.

Prevailing winds account largely for these irregular plots of arid and semiarid land, but there is scarcely a square mile on the Earth's surface where no form of life is possible. Wilfred Thresiger crossed

AS9-22-3394

A high plateau crosses the Sahara desert. The dark areas in this view of southern Algeria are exposed rock and the light areas are alluvium. The copper-hued area in the lower left is a sand dune field. A number of lines here, as well as the distinct edge of the rock formation at top, are probably faults or faultline scarps. Occasional cloudbursts sometimes turn dry riverbeds into sluices carrying sediment to lowlands.

The Sahara is 1000 miles wide and 3000 miles long. This photo, taken while a spacecraft was above the Ahnet and Ahaggar Mountains in southern Algeria, shows long, dry streambeds that probably follow faults. The arid plateau is underlain by Cretaceous limestone and has been moderately deformed by basin-and-swell movements accompanied by faulting. Wind erosion has left many closed basins in the desert here.

AS9-19-3034

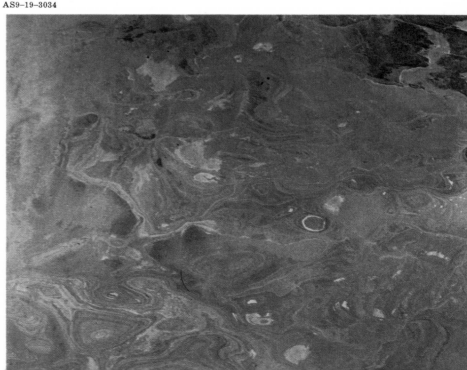

AS9-23-3530

Here is part of the Rebiana Sand Sea on the Tropic of Cancer in Libya. The dark blotches are complex volcanic rock formations that tower over the sand dunes in Algeria and Libya. The wriggly line through part of the volcanic plateau is a dry streambed. There are often deeply eroded valleys in the Sahara's highlands, and the tremendous sweeps of shifting dunes have often resulted from disintegration of ancient sandstones.

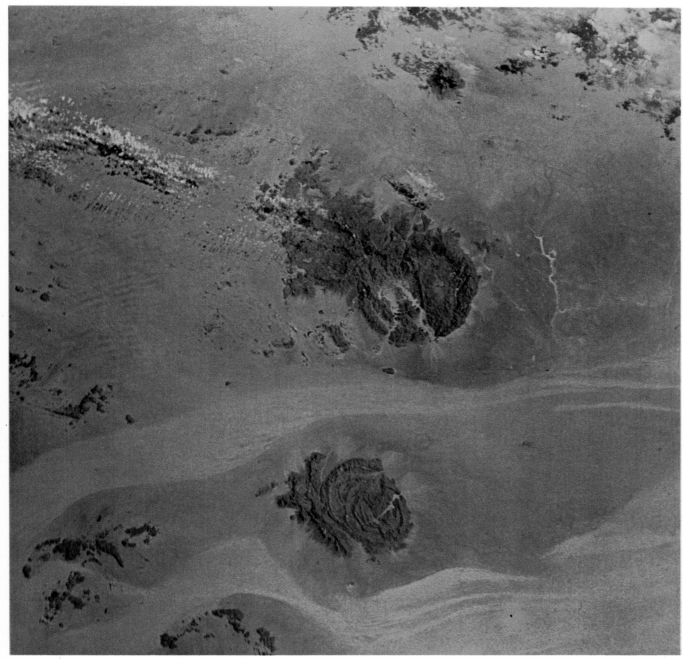

AS9-23-3533

The sands of Africa sweep like ocean currents between the mountains in the desert where the boundaries of Libya, the Sudan, and the United Arab Republic meet. The Jabal al Uweinat, a large granite igneous intrusion, in the center here is in the Sudan and rises 6256 feet. The smaller one below it is in Egypt and 4700 feet high. A few small clouds cast shadows on this area the day this photo was taken. Here the Sahara lives up to the Arabic meaning of its name, "brown and empty."

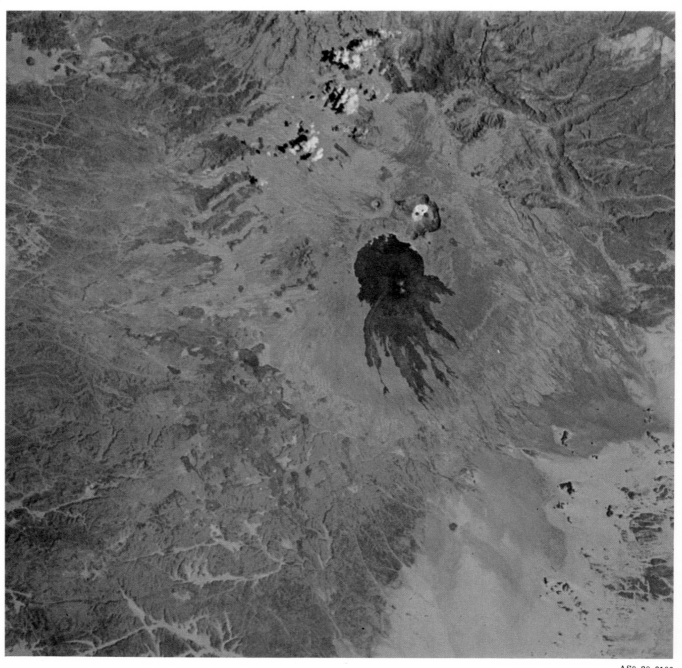

AS9-20-3106

A recently active volcano 10 712 feet high, called Pic Touside,
produced this squidlike blob on the Sahara's worn face; the
tentacles below it are lava flows. Above it is a caldera in
which there is a salt lake white enough to be mistaken for
snow. It has sharper edges than the tiny white clouds in the
sky. This scene was recorded over the Tibesti Mountains in
Libya and Chad.

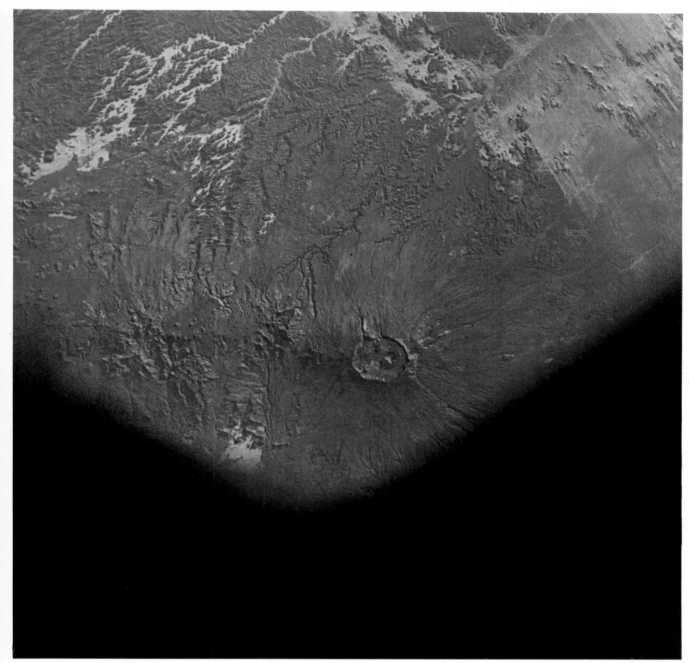

AS7–5–1621

The highest point (11 204 feet) in the Sahara is the immense Emi Koussi volcano in the Tibesti Mountains of Chad. Here, the *Encyclopaedia Britannica* explains, "eruptive rocks have forced their way through a substratum of crystalline rocks covered by horizontal Silurian grits, the scarp of which is quite brusque above the surrounding plains." Europeans partly explored the Tibesti Mountains in 1870, but not until 1915 did anyone return to map the area shown in this vertical view.

the Arabian Peninsula's grim Empty Quarter in the 1940's, and reported in *Arabian Sands*:

A cloud gathers, the rain falls, men live; the cloud disperses without rain, and men and animals die . . . there is no rhythm of the seasons, no rise and fall of sap . . . only the changing temperature marks the passage of years. It is a bitter, desiccated land which knows nothing of gentleness or ease. Yet men have lived there since earliest times. Passing generations have left fire-blackened stones at camping sites, a few faint tracks on the polished gravel plains. Elsewhere the wind wipes out their footprints. Men live there because it is the world into which they were born.

Some plants and animals have survived through all the droughts in all the blemishes on the Earth's countenance. Even the vast Sahara is littered with remnants of ancient cultures. Some of the astronauts listed it among the most photogenic parts of the globe, and to a tourist from another planet some of the arid regions might seem more inviting than the Mississippi Valley's thousands of square miles of cornfields.

Men and women born and reared in crowded cities now often find the deserts alluring, too. Since oil has been discovered beneath their sands in some places, entrepreneurs as well as artists and persons seeking solitude have been drawn to them. As more has been learned about the world, scientists also have found the deserts' mysteries increasingly absorbing. In those parts of the Earth's crust, ecologists may find fresh clues to the effects of an environment on living creatures, and vice versa.

Major deserts occur on five of the Earth's continents. In northern Chile, where the Tropic of Capricorn crosses South America, the Atacama Desert shown here separates the Pacific from the Andes Mountains. Antofagasta, a provincial capital, is just below the farther edge of the peninsula. Stratus clouds and high humidity are often noted along this shore. The basins are saline, and nitrate compounds are obtained here.

AS7-4-1592

AS9-20-3157

This great hook in the western coast of South America is Peru's Bahia de Sechura. The dark patch on the end of the peninsula is relatively high bedrock, and the light brown plain around it is the Desierto de Sechura. The dark tracks to the sea across this desert are vegetation in the river valleys. The waters over this part of the continental shelf off South America are famous for big game fishing.

This is the western coast of Australia, showing Shark Bay and Denham Sound. Near Carnarvon, a city on Shark Bay at the mouth of the Gascoyne River, there is a NASA tracking station for manned space flights. The large island in the bay is Peron Pen, and the light area near the sea above it is Lake McLeod.

AS7-8-1907

AS7-11-1980

The Ganges Plain begins at the base of the snow-covered Himalayas. Here the Ghaghara, Gandak, and Son Rivers contribute to the Ganges water that Hindus downstream consider sacred. The Ganges is a perennial and braided river that drains evergreen forests near the mountains and continues across a flood plain to savanna. This photo includes parts of Nepal, Tibet, Pakistan, and India.

84

In the 1930's, a British physicist, Ralph A. Bagnold, studied the elemental interplay between sand and wind, both in the Libyan desert and in manmade wind tunnels. Instead of chaos, he found an amazing amount of geometric order. "In places," he wrote, "vast accumulations of sand weighing millions of tons move inexorably, in regular formation, over the surface of the country, growing, retaining their shape, even breeding, in a manner which by its grotesque imitation of life is vaguely disturbing to an imaginative mind."

The Rivers' Role

In photographs of even the driest parts of our planet, one often sees the beds of drainage channels left there in the wake of rare precipitation. If there were no uplifting forces within the Earth, the rivers that rush down from the highlands of the continents, and proceed more slowly across the plains, might eventually rob them of much of their beauty as well as their soil. In the United States, rivers are estimated to be reducing the average altitude of mountainous areas about 20 inches every thousand years, and that of low regions about an inch.

When seen from orbital distances, rivers often seem to wander as randomly as drunkards, redistributing vegetation and other forms of life, and revealing innumerable variations in the contour of the land. Many overflow their banks at times and leave their old beds for new ones. Many have terraced sides, like shelves, along their flood plains. Both those exposures of the Earth's crust and the horseshoe-shaped ponds often seen alongside meandering rivers contain clues to bygone events, from which much can be deduced about the possible future behavior of a river during both dry periods and heavy run-off or flooding. River behavior is a complex matter, however, particularly when dams, drainage projects, levee construction, and other manmade factors modify natural behavior.

Rivers have both abetted men's activities and washed away whole communities, and still do. Men have been building dikes and dams to manage streams ever since the Egyptians learned to control the Nile's waters to some extent. Many streams have now been curbed, straightened, deepened, and their waters diverted to storage reservoirs, from which their energy can be drawn as desired to turn factory wheels and to irrigate previously unusable land, but this has often been done without adequate knowledge of all of the possible side effects.

Some irrigated fields are more productive now than naturally moistened areas, because they are protected not only from droughts but also from sometimes excessive rainfall. Men, however, have turned many rivers into offensive sewers, polluted beautiful natural lakes, and made dust bowls out of some formerly productive parts of the world in their haste to exploit its resources. Both in our own and in less developed countries, the welfare of future generations depends largely now on the ways in which governments permit rivers to be used. The casual indifference to river management that could be tolerated in a village culture is clearly unacceptable in a time of growing population densities and increasingly harmful effluents.

Most biologists find it difficult to imagine a way in which life could have evolved without water. Rivers provided the highways by which civilizations first advanced across continents. Whether a stream jeopardizes one's property or flows down some precipice or slope to produce power to ease one's work, it is a factor in determining the quality of human life.

For the first time in history, synoptic observations of the Earth's peaks, hills, dales, and plains, its wet and dry lands, and its forested and barren regions are economically feasible now. The pictures of some of the mountain ranges, some of the deserts, and some of the valleys that the Apollo astronauts took contain only meager hints of what can be learned when men and instruments regularly and frequently scan whole regions simultaneously. Gaps in the technical literature that account for some of the differences between theories regarding the Earth can be narrowed with the help of spacecraft, and data on which engineers rely when tackling problems of immediate social importance can be kept up to date more surely.

The pictures of the continents taken by the astronauts in the 1960's suggest both what delicately balanced mechanisms have made the Earth habitable and how feebly mankind has touched the sleeve of nature's greatness thus far. Seeing these pictures has made many reflective people grateful for having been born in the 20th century. Never before could anyone see so much of the Earth so vividly.

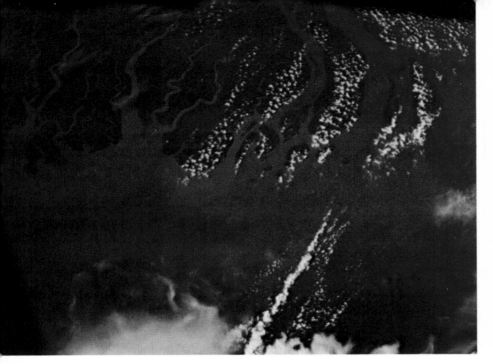

AS7-6-1675

AS6-2-941

The Ganges River has many mouths, and here they line the northern end of the Bay of Bengal. The river collects and distributes sediment for about 1500 miles between the Himalayas and the bay. From time to time great changes have occurred in this river's bed, and continued orbital observation may enhance understanding of the hydrological phenomena. The bay is shallow here, but a canyon extends out into it from the river mouths.

This nearly vertical view of the Senegal suggests how an international boundary may change when it is a meandering stream. The Senegal flows from highlands in the southern part of the Sahara to enter the Atlantic near Africa's westernmost tip. It separates southern Mauritania from Senegal. This view includes Kaédi, a trading center. Grades are gentle thereabouts, the river has many distributary channels, and some parts of its valley are farmed.

The Volta River drains part of Africa south of the Sahara. This reptilian figure is Lake Volta. Although Portuguese explorers encountered the Volta River's mouth in the 15th century, geographers did not begin to explore its upper reaches until the 19th century. Ghana now bases its hopes for industrialization largely on this river. Satellite photography can show engineers such a drainage system as a whole, and help them determine better the possible effects of changes.

AS6-2-967

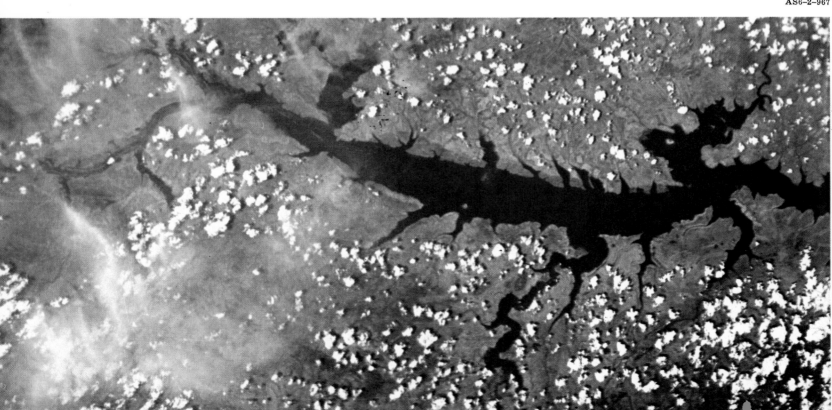

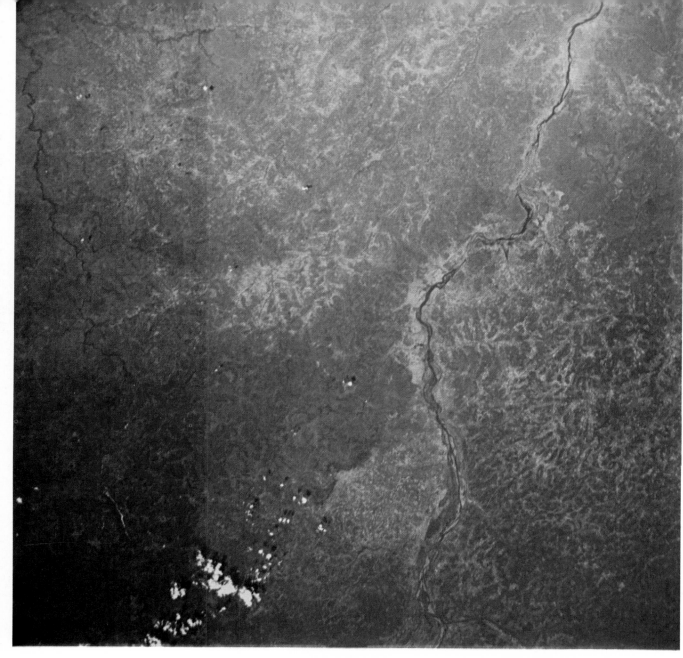

AS6-2-952

Although the Niger is only the third largest of Africa's rivers, it offers one of the best water routes to the continent's interior. This picture was taken over Bamako, the capital of Mali, a landlocked state. The Niger is 1300 feet wide in some places, 2600 miles long, and drains an area the size of Alaska.

Upstream from Bamako, the Niger flows along the southern edge of the Sahara in the vicinity of Timbuktu. The dark, straight lines visible near the Niger were the result of the river's flooding of stabilized sand dunes; there are also small lakes along the river. The Niger separates the barren lands of northern Africa from the heavily vegetated south.

AS9-19-3052

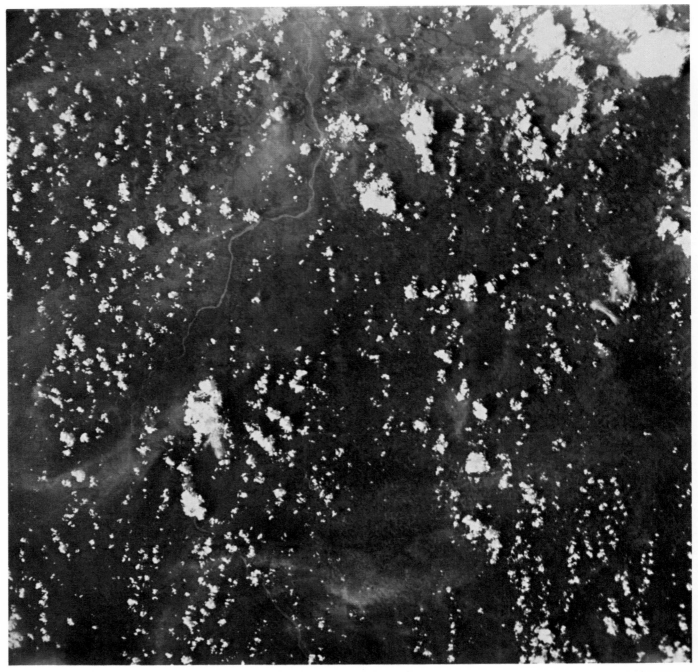

AS6-2-1006

About 4 degrees below the Equator, the Wamba and the Kwango Rivers, visible in this picture of the Congo (Kinshasa), merge to join the Kwilu, which then merges with the Kasai, which joins the Congo River to flow on to the Atlantic. These are rivers that few have ever seen. The photo also shows smoke rising from fires in the woodlands of western Africa, distinguishable from the white clouds by its grayness.

AS7-8-1914

The Zambezi River flows east across Africa to the Indian Ocean. This is its mouth at Mozambique. Mangrove swamps, intermittent rain forests, and savanna grasses cover this part of Africa's shore. The light arrowlike streaks over the land are smoke, and the brown hues of the ocean near the land are produced by sediment. Dr. David Livingstone went up and down this river in the 1850's, and a *New York Herald* reporter's search for him made Africa a romantic land to many Americans.

AS7-5-1643

Columbus discovered the Orinoco River's mouth (and thought this river might lead to Paradise), but its source was not definitely located until 1951. The Orinoco flows east across Venezuela to enter the Atlantic south of Trinidad. This is how it appears more than 200 miles upstream, where Ciudad Bolivar now serves as the commercial and communication center for the Orinoco basin. This is a sedimentary plateau with dense forest stands here and there along the meandering river.

90

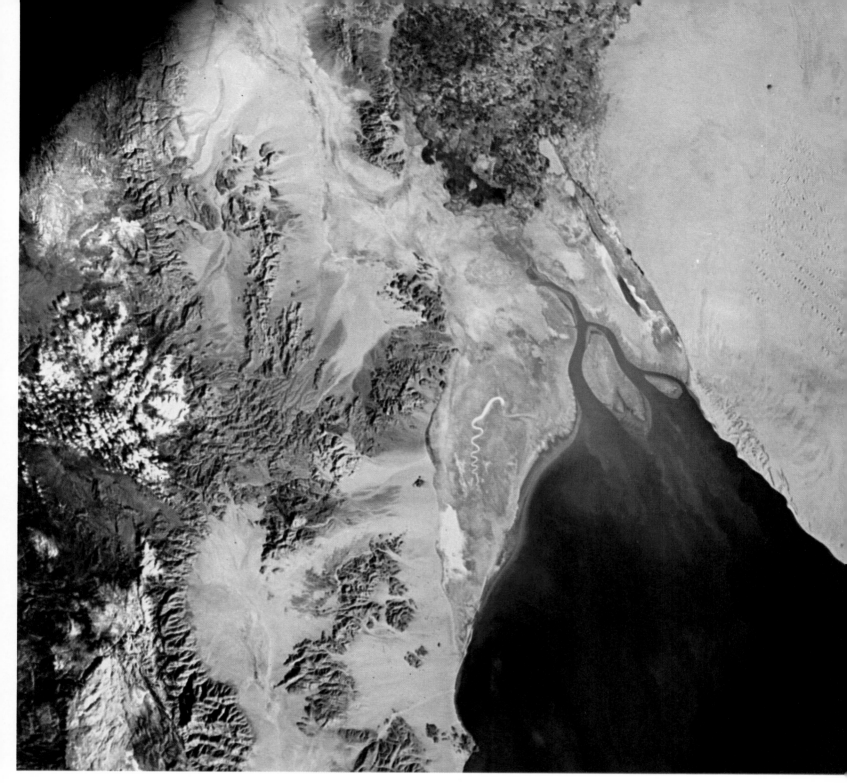

AS9-26A-3781A

Few parts of the world have been photographed as well and often from space as the Colorado River's entrance to the Gulf of California. This is a color infrared picture of its delta. Cultivated land along the river can be distinguished at the top. The Colorado is an exotic river; after rising in an area that receives abundant moisture, it flows deeply entrenched through an arid region with few tributaries.

91

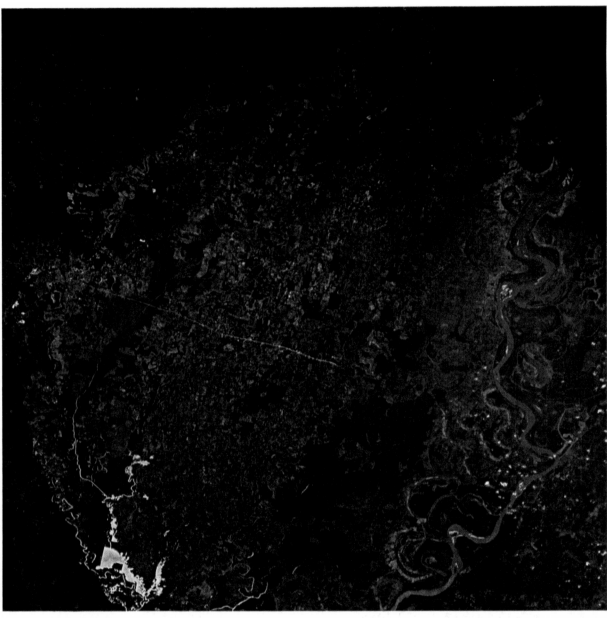

AS9-21-3302

This vertical photo of the Mississippi River flood plain in the vicinity of Monroe, La., was taken early in the spring. Urban and industrial areas are at the left, and the twisting and turning river is at the right. The very fine straight line across the center, and others elsewhere, are transportation routes and canals built by men.

The oblique photo of the Mississippi Valley at the right was taken in the fall of the year. The view extends north from the vicinity of Alexandria, La., and Jackson, Miss. A smoke plume is visible at Vidalia, La. Trees flourish in the bottomlands and fertile fields on each side of the river are intensively cultivated. This was the first great artery between the continent's heartland and the Gulf of Mexico, and determining the river's length was long a problem to surveyors. You can see why here—and also why part of this area was chosen as a test site for an experiment designed to ascertain the usefulness of space photos to managers of the Earth's resources.

92

AS7-8-1916

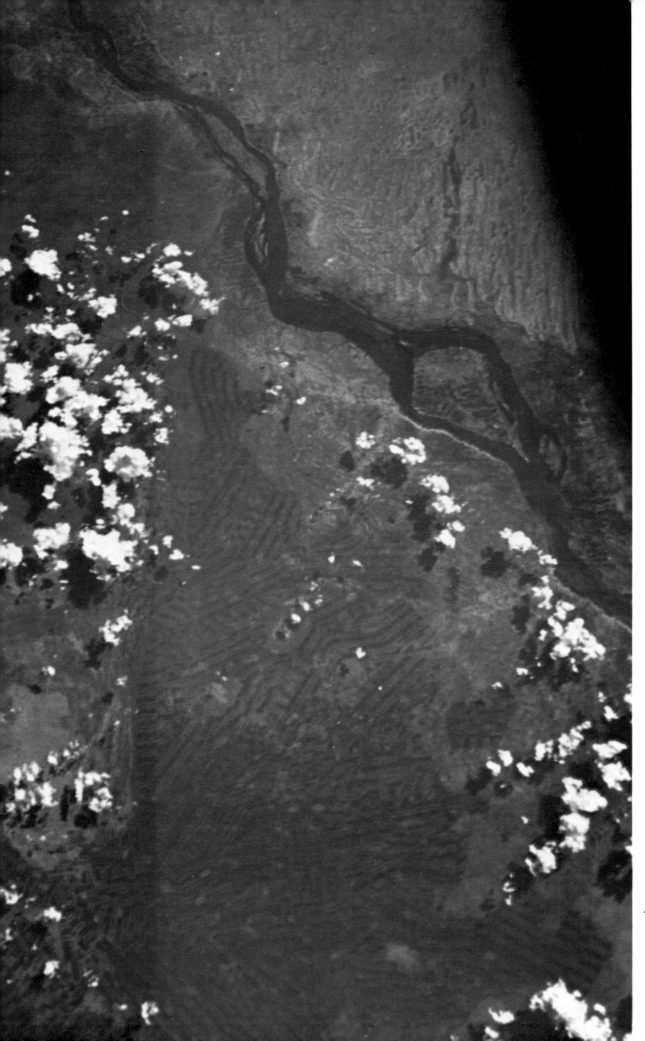

Although the marks that men make on the Earth are relatively shallow, many of them are visible from a spacecraft orbiting our island planet. The river here is in Africa, and those dark straight lines below it are irrigated cotton fields in Sudan south of Khartoum. After flowing across an alluvial flood plain, the Blue Nile and the White Nile merge near Khartoum to cross the desert of Egypt. The Nile system drains nearly 1 300 000 square miles of land. Since the time of Amenemhet I, men have managed the Nile's flow to some extent.

AS7-6-1718

5

The Hand of Man

The nation behaves well if it treats the natural resources as assets which it must turn over to the next generation increased and not impaired in value.
—THEODORE ROOSEVELT

NIGHT AFTER NIGHT in 1970, a national TV news program featured events that posed the question: "Can the world be saved?" Wherever the television camera turned, it seemed, the fish, the birds, the swamps, the shores, or some other natural feature was imperiled by the ubiquitous hand of man. Scarcely any part of terra firma looked quite as firm to the reporters as it formerly did.

Man's impact on his planet must have been exceedingly small at first. Plowing that disturbs only the top 10 inches of soil leaves but faint scratches on a globe almost 8000 miles in diameter. Yet when vast areas are plowed for cultivation in the geometric patterns that are implicit in property lines, the hand of man becomes evident from orbital altitudes.

Increasing the number of the world's arable acres, and making that soil more productive per acre, has permitted the population to soar. Population trends have indicated that by A.D. 2000 there may be twice as many human beings to be fed as the Earth has arable acres. By then, the face of our planet will surely bear more obvious evidence of our presence.

The Cornell astronomer, Carl Sagan, has noted that from an observatory on Mars with telescopes like those on Earth—

seasonal variations of [our planet's] cultivated crops and deciduous forests would probably be observable, but varying interpretations of these phenomena would probably be found. The greatest engineering feats would be largely invisible, and the lights of the largest cities would only be marginally detectable at night. Nuclear explosions would be observable, but their short duration would result in many escaping detection, and almost all evading corroboration.

A scientist no better armed with knowledge of the Earth than that, consequently, might have to circle our globe many times, and possibly land on it, to distinguish between the work of mankind and the patterns of nature. Even from quite short distances outside the Earth's envelope of air, its solid crust at first appears to be "a mighty maze without a plan." Inanimate, biological, and social phenomena are so intermingled in most pictures of the Earth's surface taken from spacecraft that men examining them have often found it difficult to recognize human handiwork.

Categorizing information about the Earth has been a challenge to geographers throughout history. They have subdivided their studies in dozens of ways, and they tend nowadays to specialize in regional, physical, agricultural, urban, political, historical, and other particular aspects of their discipline. The variety of things visible on the Earth, however, and the complex relationships that continue to be discovered among the observable phenomena, have made it hard for professional geographers to categorize new information about our planet. "Even after laborious research by many scholars," Prof. Richard Hartshorne, an eminent member of the Association of American Geographers, wrote in 1959, "it may not be possible to separate features of the Earth resulting from nature exclusive of man from those that result primarily from man."

A few generations ago the organization of information about the Earth seemed to be a relatively minor problem that could be left to academicians. People struggling to tame wildernesses were not inclined to fret about such matters. Other tasks came first. But now civilization's advance has so spread the extent of human activities that their effects have become a matter of deep concern to thoughtful men and women everywhere. Young Americans observed an Earth Day in 1970 for the first time.

The Earth's gifts to our species of life, many persons are realizing belatedly, will not last forever if we use them too wastefully. The per capita use of the Earth's riches has soared in all nations. The U.S. Department of the Interior has warned repeatedly that at present rates of consumption, the known reserves of copper, lead, zinc, and other minerals may be exhausted in a few more decades. Conservation of forests has become essential to meeting the demands for lumber. Hydrologists emphasize that water already has become a limiting resource in some parts of the world. The United Nations Food and Agriculture Organization estimates that three times as much food will be needed by the dawn of the next century as is being produced now. Hence the need for accurate knowledge of the amount and distribution of natural resources on our planet has become increasingly urgent.

Yet Prof. Carroll L. Wilson, who directed a 1970 summer study of critical environment problems for the Massachusetts Institute of Technology, states:

Relevant data on critical global problems are very poor, and this seriously limits our understanding of their meaning. Far better estimates well into the 21st century are needed in order to assess the expected impact of man on the world ecological system to give us time to take action to avoid crisis or catastrophe.

A closed life-support system would be essential to men embarking on long journeys to other planets.

The problem of providing food, water, and breathable air to astronauts on such trips and recycling and regenerating waste products is clearly analogous to the work we must do to protect the Earth's environment. Research undertaken to continue the exploration of the solar system may also help us meet the difficult technical challenges here on Earth created by the rising population, growing heaps of waste matter, and polluted air and water.

Some biologists and sociologists have warned, on the basis of our present meager knowledge, that human intrusions on natural processes may so affect the planet that large parts of the world will cease to be habitable. Conceivably, therefore, new aids to gaging the impact of the hand of man on the Earth may have become available to us in the very nick of time. In the 1970's a series of unmanned earth resources satellites is scheduled to be launched into orbits that will permit much more of the globe to be observed than was photographed from the Gemini and Apollo vehicles. These satellites, moreover, will carry sophisticated new sensing devices that are superior for many purposes to cameras such as the astronauts have carried.

Prior Knowledge Helps Interpreters

Visitors to New York City usually find that it is easier to comprehend the shape and size of Manhattan Island from the top of the Empire State Building than it is from the snarls in the streets. For the same reason, some aspects of the Earth may be more obvious to an observer far above them than to an inquirer in a valley.

The first camera that a balloon carried aloft at Paris in 1859 was a new tool for the study of urban, rural, and remote areas. Growing use of aerial photography has taken place in this century, and many parts of the world have been photographed from airplanes for the planners and managers of its resources to examine. Faster progress has been made than ever before in the use of airborne sensors to predict crop yields, locate promising areas for oil drilling, and to foresee potential threats to our lives and welfare.

By taking overlapping pictures, stereoscopic images of the land are obtained, and contour maps improved. By using various bands of the electromagnetic spectrum to record images, ways have been found to make certain features stand out more

ASWAN DAM

AS9-20-3177

Lake Nasser, a long, immense body of water backed up by the Aswan Dam, dominates the foreground of this view of Egypt. The Red Sea is on the horizon. The arrows point to the damsite. Construction of this dam was a stimulus to Egypt's economy, but it already has apparently affected the regional ecology. Fishing in the Mediterranean has reportedly been influenced because the dam holds back water containing mineral nutrients.

97

distinctly than the way they appear in the light to which human eyes respond. By painstakingly piecing together photos of small areas taken sequentially from aircraft, mosaics of large regions have been placed on the walls of geographers, geologists, and civil engineers. More recently, by using digital computers to analyze and selectively enhance photographic images, the usefulness of cameras at extremely high altitudes has been further extended. (There is an example on p. 61.)

Most of the technology developed for aerial surveys is also helpful in surveys from space. A single picture that shows a whole region at one instant is often superior to a mosaic of pictures taken of parts of it from different points in different light at different times. Mississippi River boat pilots learned long ago, Mark Twain wrote, to view its surface from "a little distance." Now the lines, tones, textures, shadows, and other elements of the whole Earth are becoming as meaningful to interpreters of space photography as the bubbles, swirls, and colors of the river were to steamboat pilots.

Our prior knowledge makes it easier for us to "read" pictures of the Earth. We are careful to distinguish between snow and clouds; we can recognize smoke from an industrial plant or a burning forest more surely than if we were studying an unknown planet. Previous knowledge tells geologists where to look for fault lines in mountains, and oceanographers where to look for currents in the oceans. Hence we are well prepared to use satellites to gather global information and thereby improve our stewardship of our planet.

When an Earth Resources Technology Satellite circles our planet in a Sun-synchronous orbit, a camera aboard it can photograph every portion of the illuminated hemisphere at the same local Sun time. The data reported by terrestrial explorers will then be enriched by information transmitted electronically from space. Changes will become apparent more quickly than they formerly could be reported by navigators, prospectors, and mountain climbers.

The data obtained in this new way also can be analyzed and distributed to scientists throughout the world more rapidly than was previously possible. This will facilitate accurate, up-to-date measurements of changes taking place both in densely populated parts of the world and areas in which men still seldom set foot.

Primitive men and early societies left pictures, inscriptions, and scrolls in languages that are no longer written or spoken, yet scholars have learned to decipher many of the messages thus bequeathed to us. Some of the pictures taken by astronauts in the 1960's were almost equally puzzling to specialists at first, but analysis of the fine lines, peculiar shapes, and different colors in them already has been highly rewarding.

An inexperienced viewer must often study a space photograph of the Earth intently to find evidence of the hand of man in it, but experience leads to clues such as these:

- An inland body of water formed by a dam is likely to have at least one sharper, more geometric edge than a natural lake.
- Canals and turnpikes constructed by men are nearly always straighter than the courses chosen and randomly changed by rivers. Old roads run directly into cities, whereas new highways circle them more often.
- The forests cleared by men differ in regularity of shape from the wounds in woodlands where lightning has struck and the wind has guided the flames.
- Tilled fields look more evenly quilted than land that has never been plowed, and are usually found in naturally moistened land or irrigated areas.
- Metropolitan areas look as if industrious insects had woven hasty webs and patches on the landscape.

For thousands of years, human beings could do but little to alter the Earth's appearance from afar. Technology recently has enabled us to do much more, and can also help us gage the effects of our handiwork. Pictures such as those in this chapter have made even casual viewers want to know more about what we are doing to the planet.

Verifiable Findings Are Illustrated

The photographs taken by the Gemini astronauts, before the Apollo flights, demonstrated the potential value of space surveys in the management of natural resources. Now more thorough and faster reconnaissance of fields, forests, and other exploitable features of the Earth became feasible. The

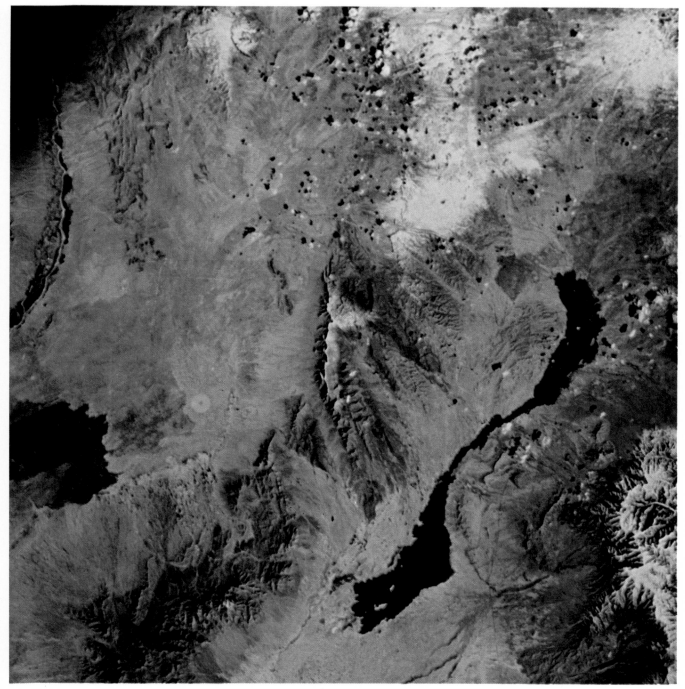

AS9-26A-3805

The tiny, obviously manmade circle in the New Mexico desert is an instrumentation site on the White Sands Missile Range, conspicuous where the weathered alkali soil was scraped away. Just to its right but short of the mountains is the Trinity site, where the world's first atomic bomb was secretly exploded on July 16, 1945.

AS7-6-1696

At the eastern end of the Mediterranean, the light hue of the desert ends in a nearly straight line, just above the center of this photograph. That is the manmade boundary between the United Arab Republic and Israel. The Dead Sea is visible almost directly above that line, and is shown from a viewpoint that is more nearly overhead on the next page.

Apollo 9 astronauts, consequently, were equipped to conduct what Prof. Robert N. Colwell of the University of California at Berkeley believes "could easily prove to be the most important photographic experiment in history."

It was both a test of recording techniques and an exercise in deciphering correctly a new kind of information. The U.S. Departments of Agriculture and of the Interior, the Environmental Science Services Administration, the U.S. Naval Oceanographic Office, and academic and industrial re-

searchers participated with NASA in this experiment, and some of the pictures in this volume resulted from it.

In addition to the hand-held Hasselblads like those that the Gemini astronauts had used, Apollo 9 carried a specially designed package of four cameras. This was done so that the same scene could be recorded at the same instant in four different wavelength bands. Features encountered on the Earth's surface tend to reflect and emit radiant energy in distinctive amounts at specific wave-

AS7-6-1698

The Dead Sea occupies a region where a block of the Earth's crust dropped below sea level. Here you can distinguish evaporating pans built at its lower end to recover chemicals from it. The Sun and wind dry the brine from the sea in those pans. Water to refine the material left is obtained from wells that tap the sands and gravels of the rift valley south of the Dead Sea.

lengths. Hence some can be detected better when photographed in particular wavelengths than in other parts of the spectrum. By comparing pictures taken in different bands much more can be learned than if the Earth were photographed in only one wavelength.

With three of the four cameras in the special package carried by Apollo 9, black-and-white imagery in three different wavelengths of light—the green, the red, and the near-infrared bands—was recorded. The fourth camera was loaded with infra-

red color film, which contains dyes responsive to all three of those wavelength bands. In the package each camera was set at the right exposure for the film behind it, and the shutters were tripped simultaneously. From the Apollo 9 pictures taken in these four different ways and from related studies, experimenters have learned a great deal about how to use space photography to evaluate fields of crops, rangeland, forests, geologic structures, and other features of the Earth.

Although often more valuable than ordinary pictures to scientists, photos taken in unfamiliar bands of light look unnatural to most of us. Healthy green fields, for example, are more prominent in black-and-white pictures taken in certain unfamiliar wavelengths of light than they are in those taken in the band on which our eyes depend, and such fields look reddish rather than green in color infrared pictures.

Similarly, oblique pictures often seem clearer to a layman than vertical views of the Earth's surface, but scientists usually can derive more helpful data from a vertical picture. The Apollo astronauts, therefore, recorded both what they saw when they looked toward the horizon and what the landscape was like when they looked directly down at it.

In addition to arranging for the Apollo 9 crew to take pictures in these various ways, the planners of their photographic experiment designated certain areas on Earth as test sites. These included parts of California, Arizona, and the Lower Mississippi Valley, chosen because a great deal was already known and in which a good many different developments could be examined.

At about the same time that the Apollo 9 lenses were focused on the test sites, aircraft flew over them at altitudes ranging from a few hundred to about 70 000 feet, recording the radiation reflected from them in various bands of light that could be recorded at those altitudes. In selected parts of those test sites, photographs also were taken on the ground, and the radiant energy from various features of the land was measured. Since repetitive photos of the same crops at different times of the year can also aid interpreters, more pictures of the same areas were taken monthly from aircraft throughout the spring and summer after the Apollo 9 flight in March.

"Ground truth" about those areas was thus determined beyond any shadow of doubt that a cloud might cast—either on the scene or in the mind of an interpreter. All this was done to enable specialists in agriculture, forestry, and other applied sciences to check the accuracy of their interpretations of the pictures brought back by Apollo 9. The findings have not only been helpful to the designers of future Earth Resources Technology Satellites, but are also being used to train students in reading space photographs and to test various devices developed to enhance the clarity of images.

From this experiment and related research, interpreters have found that it is possible to recognize many crops by the seasonal and other variations in the looks of a farmer's fields from above the atmosphere. Side effects of using rivers to irrigate land, and producing electric power from the energy of their waters, can also be studied. Some kinds of pollution of the air, and of the oceans near shorelines, can be quickly spotted now. Further advances in technology are likely to increase the usefulness of satellites in monitoring the Earth's resources.

To the surprise of many viewers, political boundaries in some parts of the world are as distinct as physical boundaries. California's Imperial Valley was one of the test sites, and the boundary between the United States and Mexico there is as clear in a color infrared photograph as if a mapmaker with a ruler had drawn it. In another Apollo picture, the wholly manmade line between two States, New Mexico and Texas, is likewise as distinct as if someone had pasted two separate pictures together there. On the opposite side of the globe, too, one sees how the look of virtually identical terrain changes with the varied uses men make of it: The land of Israel has a different hue than the desert in the United Arab Republic. Many boundaries between states and nations are indistinguishable from space, but wherever they follow rivers they can be traced, and changes in the riverbeds can be noted in vertical pictures taken from above a clear sky.

The professional geographers' goal has long been to produce "an accurate, orderly, and rational interpretation of the variable character of the Earth's surface." Space photography already has revealed many errors in their best maps and surveys; some mountains and some islands are not quite where they were supposed to be until they were photographed simultaneously with other landmarks. How far some cities have spread out over the land can also be seen better in some pictures than in the maps now available.

The space pictures taken in the 1960's, however, give only glimpses of further giant steps in technology that scientists envision. Much work remains to be done to attain the geographers' goal. Meanwhile, these pictures may somewhat deepen many men's understanding of "how our terrestrial home is constructed, the meaning of its scenery, and the pattern of its sky."

AS9-26A-3807

A vertical line down the center of this color infrared photo is the boundary between New Mexico and Texas. The difference in the Earth's appearance to the left and right of that line has been ascribed to different practices in those States in the use of well water for irrigation. Most of the vegetation was dormant when this picture was taken.

103

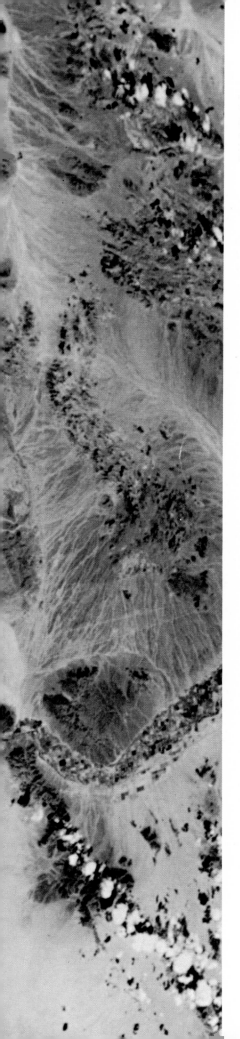

AS9-26A-3698A

Tiny red squares in the color infrared photo at the left are farm fields. Those far to the left are in California's Imperial Valley between the Salton Sea and Mexico. At the international border, the coloring changes; Calexico and Mexicali are light areas at the border. A fine grayish line that runs east from the valley is the All-American Canal. The Colorado River is in the right half of the picture.

The Imperial Valley also was photographed in ordinary light (below) during the Apollo 9 photographic experiment. Arid areas near it then looked yellowish rather than white. The boundary between the United States and Mexico was perceptible, but was not nearly as distinct as when color infrared film was used.

AS9-21-3287

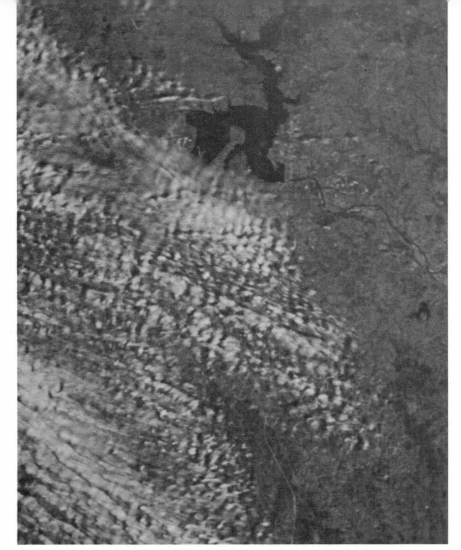

AS9-20-3146

An experienced viewer can recognize men's handiwork in all four photos here. The dark, fancy figure at the left is Lake Texoma on the border between Texas and Oklahoma. Its wide lower tentacle looks sliced off. That is the site of Denison Dam, and the stream below the dam is a dark line. A light, nearly vertical line at the bottom of this picture is a road that leads to Dallas.

The picture below includes Mexico City and some of the volcanoes (dark areas) that surround it. The geometric roundness of a large dot in the lower center suggests that it is manmade. In fact it is a part of a drainage system. A canal runs from it to the bottom of this view.

AS9-19-3012

Notice the two large inland reservoirs in the photo of the Carolina coast at the right. The Santee Dam gave one of them, Lake Marion, a sharp edge. The more circular body of water nearby is Lake Moultrie. The prominent rivers are the Santee, the Black, and the Pee Dee. Charleston, S.C., is at the right.

Several little rectangles are the clearest evidence of men's presence in the picture below of clouds and rivers of North Carolina. Those rectangles are cleared areas at the Fort Bragg Military Reservation. To the right of them you can see how the Neuse River and creeks that feed it drain the scattered woodlands and fields of the coastal plain.

AS9-23-3553

AS6-2-1443

AS6-2-1467

In this photo of the rugged land of southwestern Arizona there are two clear clues to men's presence. Can you find them? The large white spot above center is the Willcox Dry Lake, produced by nature. But above and below it are little rectangles, which indicate that parts of this valley are farmed. Near the lower edge of the picture you can see the white plume from a smokestack near Douglas, Ariz.

The red scrawl at the top here is the Red River. The rectangle above it is an airport near Shreveport, La. The fine, white, vertical line is Highway 80 running east from Shreveport. Practice analysis with pictures like this, where "ground truth" is readily available, is one excellent method of training photo interpreters.

108

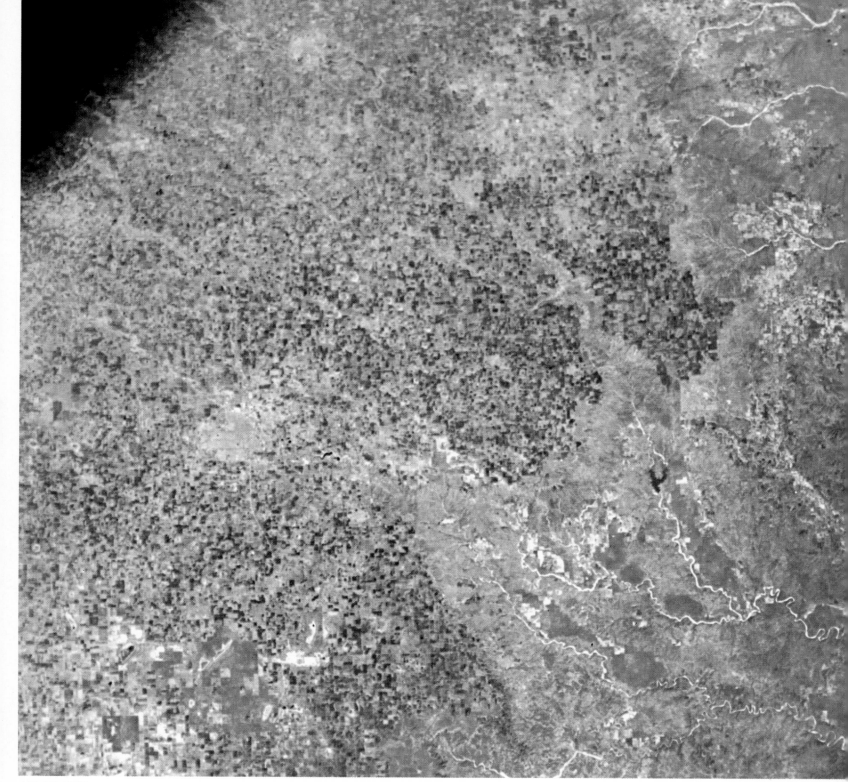

AS9–26A–3808A

The quilting in the upper part of this color infrared photo is cultivated
land around Lubbock, Tex. The fields would look red if they were
photographed with the same film when crops were mature. In the right
portion of the picture are parts of the White and Pease River systems
that drain the Cap Rock Escarpment. From this part of Texas, the
Great Plains extend all the way to Canada.

109

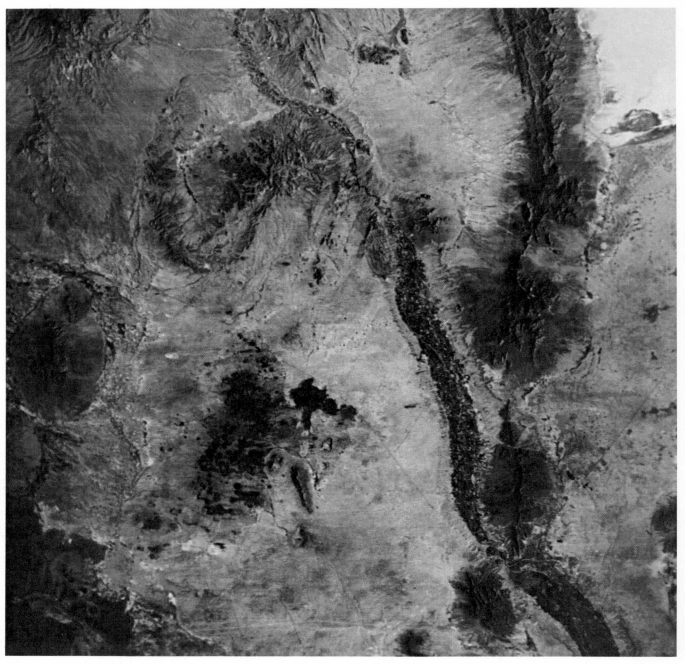

AS6-2-1447

The long diagonal strip down this picture is cultivated land in the Rio Grande Valley. This is a nearly vertical look at the Tularosa Valley (at right). The White Sands National Monument is in the upper right, and El Paso in the lower right. Interpreters studying this photo closely have recognized straight lines in it as railroads and highways, including the Southern Pacific's single-track, 50-foot roadbed, but to a casual observer nature's work is more obvious than that of men.

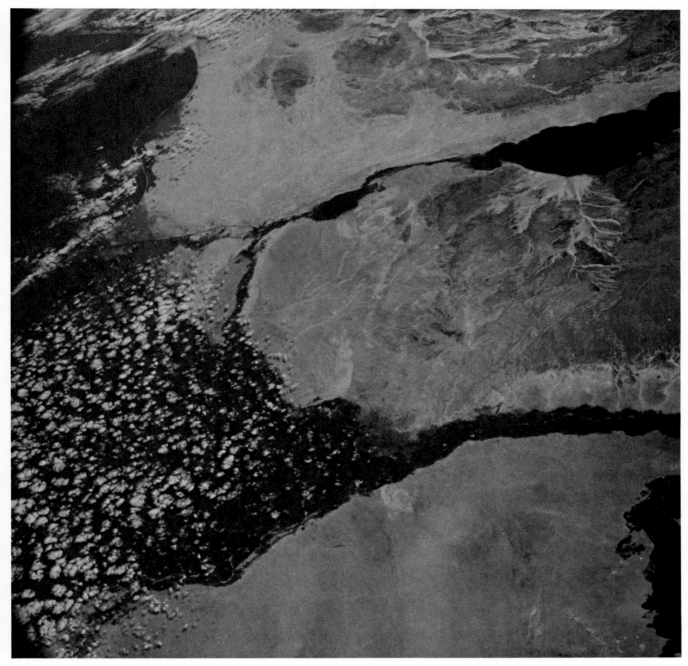

AS9-23-3521

The big dark triangle is the Nile Delta. The broad ribbon that leads across the photo to it is a river valley in which men have dwelt for millennia. Cairo is in the center of the picture, where that ribbon begins to broaden. Paralleling the Nile is the Suez Canal, between the Mediterranean Sea and the Gulf of Suez. Close scrutiny of photos such as this has proven helpful to geographers studying patterns of settlement.

AS7-8-1918

The light area to the left of this long bay is Mobile, Ala. A narrow plume of smoke is being wafted out over the Gulf of Mexico from a point below it. The water of Mobile Bay is darkened by sediment carried down from Alabama's highlands and across its coastal plain. Some of this sediment can be seen escaping into the gulf through the entrance to the bay in the foreground.

AS7–11–2022

The gray haze below the white clouds approaching the western coast of
North America here is the smog of Los Angeles, the largest city in
California. Beyond the mountains east of it are the Mojave Desert and
the San Joaquin Valley. The San Andreas Fault forms the western
boundary of the Mojave Desert. The clouds toward the horizon are over
the Western Cordillera. (There are two more views of Los Angeles in
the next chapter.)

113

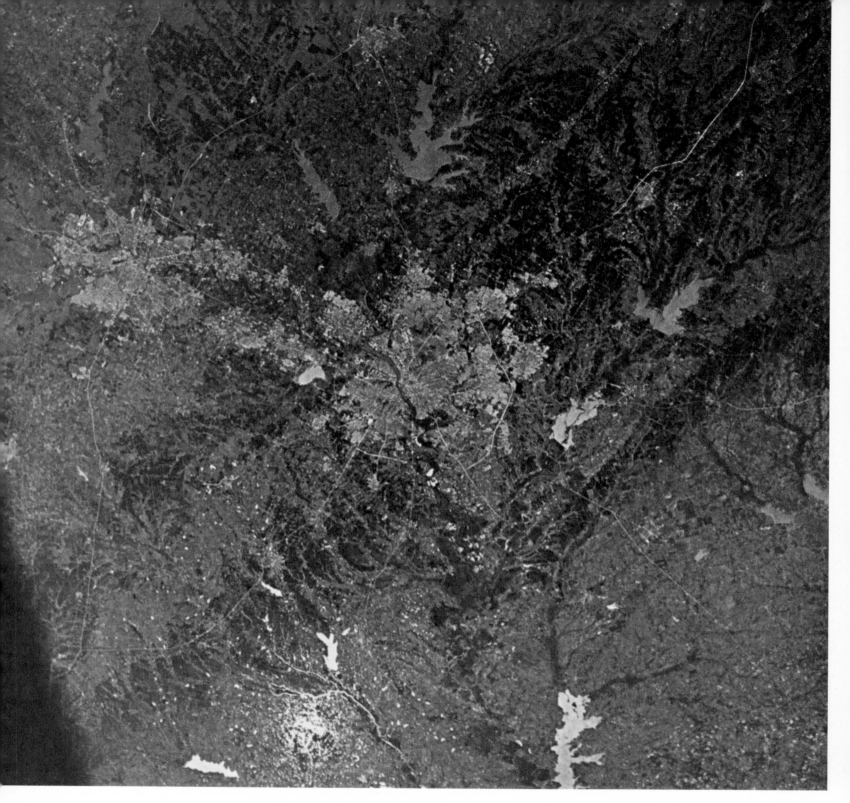

AS9-21-3299

More people now live in urban areas than ever before. About 2 million persons dwell in the two light and plainly connected areas in the center of this photograph. Those areas are Fort Worth and Dallas, Tex., and their suburbs. From photographs like this, skilled interpreters using image-enhancement devices can chart urban growth more rapidly than it is currently being recorded and displayed on maps. Reservoirs, rivers, and highways in the environs of these cities are plainly visible.

AS–26A–3801A

Phoenix, Ariz., is slightly to the right of the center of this color infrared picture taken as part of the Apollo 9 photographic experiment. Analysts have estimated that 5 percent of the area shown is urban now, 20 percent used for agriculture, 43 percent serving as rangeland, 24 percent taken up by mountains and uplands, and 8 percent occupied by water courses. The 1970 census showed a 45.2-percent increase in the population of Maricopa County (Phoenix). Notice the clustering along the rivers.

115

AS9-26A-3798A

San Diego's hook-shaped harbor interrupts the smooth curve of North America's western shore between San Clemente, Calif., and Baja California in this color infrared photo. When it was taken, snow still lay on the Peninsular Ranges south of Palomar Mountain. Those ranges are from 20 to 40 miles wide, broken into ridges and spurs, and cut by numerous faults.

6
Across North America

NORTH AMERICA is the third largest of the Earth's continents, and is believed to have been the third one to be explored and populated by primitive men. Those men who spread across our continent from the northwest tens of thousands of years ago could see that the Moon was round, but not what lay beyond the receding horizon ahead of them. Those Europeans who approached the continent from the south five centuries ago had reason to think that the Earth also was round, but could only speculate about its far side.

Vasco Núñez de Balboa did not know how big a thing he was talking about when he swaggered across the Isthmus of Panama in 1513 and claimed the whole Pacific Ocean for Castille. Ten years later Giovanni de Verazona, a mariner and surveyor serving the king of France, believed that the land he glimpsed beyond Pamlico Sound from Cape Hatteras was the mainland of Asia. For many more decades the geographers' knowledge of North America was as meager as the information that Immanuel Kant assembled—without ever venturing more than 60 miles from home—to conceive the nebular hypothesis.

But gradually the exploration of America continued, and men confined to the shores, rivers, and forest trails increased the data available to mapmakers. Closing the gaps took many years. Crossing the continent required months, then weeks, and then days until very recently. Now people cross it in a few hours, some of them without even noticing the clouds and land below. Only a few astronauts, however, have seen both the Pacific and Atlantic shores outside their window at the same instant.

The Apollo 9 crew of James McDivitt, David Scott, and Russell Schweikart crossed North America in about 10 minutes. It was their homeland, they had often flown over it, and they recognized many landmarks. Their primary task was to test equipment for a lunar landing, and public attention was focused on the maneuvers of the command module (Gumdrop) and the lunar module (Spider). Nevertheless, while circling the world 150 times for this purpose, the crew photographed parts of five continents, including areas in North America designated for special observation by scientists seeking better ways to monitor the Earth's resources.

Some of the finest photographs of our country that the Apollo 9 trio brought back were chosen to illustrate preceding chapters. The pictures in this chapter were selected to show the United States from the vantage point of astronauts. (A few of these views extend into Mexico, one of the countries cooperating with NASA in studies of space photography.) All of these photographs are of sights that airline passengers glance at every day from lower altitudes.

Three distinct, important parts of our country—its Western Cordillera, its Central Prairies, and its Eastern Seaboard—can be examined here. Astronauts have not yet photographed all of our 50

117

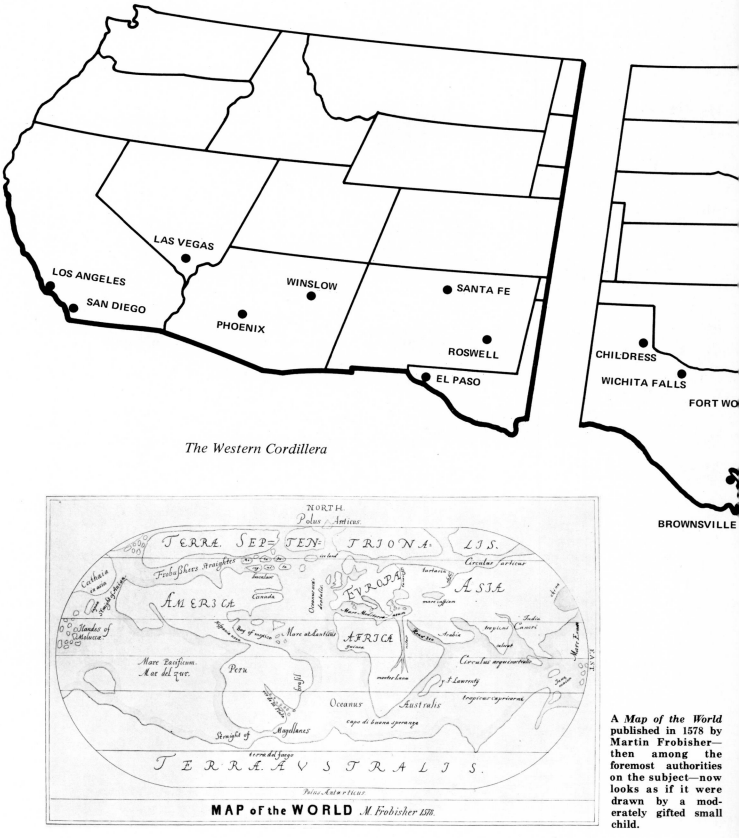

The Western Cordillera

LOS ANGELES

SAN DIEGO

LAS VEGAS

PHOENIX

WINSLOW

SANTA FE

ROSWELL

EL PASO

CHILDRESS

WICHITA FALLS

FORT WO

BROWNSVILLE

NORTH.
Polus Articus.

TERRA. SEP=TEN=TRIONA=LIS.

ice land

Cathaia in asia

Frobußhers Straightes

bacalaos

Circulus Articus.

tartaria

ASIA

AMER3CA

Canada

Oceanus deltatius

EVROPA

mare calpium

Ajan

Ilandes of Molucca.

Bay of mexico

Mare at lanticus

Mare Mediteraneum

AFRICA

guinea

Red Sea

Arabia

India

tropicus Cancri

calcicut

Mare Iuuum

EAST

Mare Pacificum.
Mar del zur.

Peru

brasil

montes Lunæ

Circulus æquinoctialis

y. S. Lawrenty

Iaua maior

Oceanus Australis

tropicus capricorni

Straight of Magellanes

capo di buona speranza

terra del fuego

TERRA. AVSTRALIS.

Polus Antarticus.

MAP of the WORLD   M. Frobisher 1578.

A *Map of the World* published in 1578 by Martin Frobisher— then among the foremost authorities on the subject—now looks as if it were drawn by a moderately gifted small child.

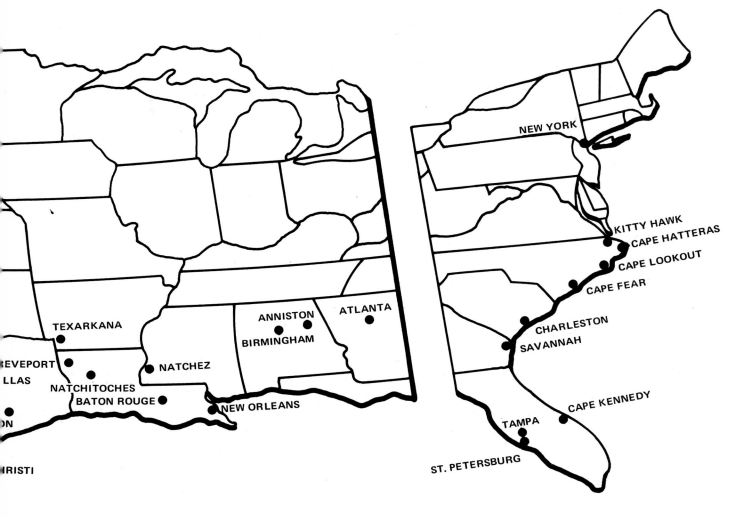

The Eastern Seaboard

From the Mountains to the Prairies

states from comparable heights. Hence these are only a sampling of the way that future generations will see the features of their native land and the relationships between some of those features. The pictures in this chapter show a relatively small part of North America as it would look to a stranger, first sighting it from high over the Pacific, while circling the Earth between 100 and 200 miles above its surface. All of these pictures were taken within 10 days from a single spacecraft.

Each one of the three regions shown is a historic, romantic part of the United States that has contributed uniquely to our country's relative affluence. The Western Cordillera is also one of the world's most scenic mountain areas. The Central Plains have yielded much of the food and fuel needed by our increasing population. The Eastern Seaboard's harbors and wetlands were the starting point for our civilization's westward movement across the continent. While aerial photographs have greatly aided in mapping and measuring portions of our land, the views that spacecraft obtained within the last decade already have given specialists a large body of additional information. They also have made it easier for all of us to visualize now why our forefathers' achievements in settling the continent required so much patience, courage, and endurance.

Civilization has been defined as a process by which human faculties are enlarged. The broader views of the Earth's continents that are attainable

119

henceforth may enhance the understanding of millions of the simplifications essential to the cartographers' art and the generalizations of historians. These views have shown many of us how little we know about some aspects of the Earth, what men have done to it, and how advantageous it will be for men to think in planetary terms. Increasing human capabilities made the space ventures possible, and those ventures are further extending the possibilities. The new perspective on our continent's past, present, and future is part of the basis for President Nixon's hope that the 1970's can become memorable "as the time when this country regained a productive harmony between man and nature."

The Western Cordillera

By far the most rugged part of the United States is the western third. Here some peaks rise more than 14 000 feet, yet Death Valley is 280 feet below sea level. From the continental shelf off southern California, eight mountaintops emerge from the great ocean as the Channel Islands. Another fringe of mountains hugs the shore. Between them and the much higher ranges farther inland, there is a splendid, productive valley. These are some of the features that stand out prominently in the astronauts' pictures.

First the railroads, then automobiles, and then airplanes accelerated the development of this once-remote region. By the 1960's, a Los Angeles mayor described his city as an over-developed land. From space the view of this city, spread over many square miles, often is obscured by substances generated by men's machinery intermixed with the moisture in the atmosphere. Still, toward the eastern horizon, one sees much the same sight that awed the bearded drivers of covered wagons in the 19th century: Vast fields of snow on mountaintops, as white as if the purest clouds were permanently anchored there.

If you were in a spacecraft speeding eastward over southern California, you would see, directly beneath you, smooth, many-colored checkerboards, deserts as bare as Mother Hubbard's cupboard, and an exotic river flowing toward a gash in the mountains. The Colorado River, like the Nile, flows down from jagged highlands and across a broad arid region, loaded with silt to build a delta. The Imperial Valley, the Salton Sea, and the river's mouth at the northern end of the Gulf of California

constitute such a beautiful composition when seen from space that the astronauts have photographed this part of the Earth many times. Spaniards called the Imperial Valley, sunk in the midst of a desert, "the Palm of the Hand of God." Scholars have since dubbed it "a geographic skeleton," "a hydrographic puzzle," and "an international headache."

When a New Orleans doctor who had crossed this barren depression on a mule first proposed that it be irrigated with water from the Colorado River, an authority on soils discouraged the idea, and a popular California wit remarked that he could see "no great obstacle except the porous nature of sand." Now this valley is the largest single area of irrigated agriculture in the Western Hemisphere, producing crops and livestock worth fortunes annually.

When in 1905 the Colorado was partly diverted into the Imperial Valley for irrigation, a catastrophic flood enlarged the diversion canal until in a few hours most of the river was pouring into the valley. Soon a 35-mile-long lake, now named the Salton Sea, occupied much of the valley, and it took 18 months of strenuous engineering effort to dam the enlarged canal, restoring proper flow. Today the area is a huge garden bowl, though there remain problems of saline sediments with which the experts are still grappling.

Upstream, space photography shows another manmade body of water, Lake Mead, near the city of Las Vegas, and more such reservoirs along other streams between the mountains. Upstream, too, of course, one sees the 6000-foot-deep Grand Canyon through which the Colorado has flowed century after century. A laconic cowboy, finding himself on its brink for the first time, is said to have exclaimed: "My God! Something has happened here!" Geologists have reacted with equal incredulity to some of the astronauts' pictures of the western mountains; in them, the scientists have detected details not shown in the maps being used to study earthquakes.

Near the Grand Canyon, the Apollo pictures also show the immensity of lava beds left by now dead volcanoes, and the great Meteor Crater in Arizona. Although almost a mile across and 600 feet deep, this huge impact scar is a mere pinprick compared to the lunar and Martian craters now being examined by spacecraft.

The Rocky Mountains are one of the Earth's

AS9–20–3134

This view of California extends into Nevada and shows the whole Sierra Nevada Range. A wet winter preceded the Apollo 9 flight in March 1969, which explains much of the whiteness. In the lower center, however, the snow made it especially easy to see the Kern Canyon Fault in the Sierras. The Mojave Desert is in the lower right, and the usually dry Rosamond and Rogers Lakes near the Edwards Air Force Base look a bit muddy.

AS9–26A–3744A

Los Angeles is at the top of this color infrared photo. A straight, nearly vertical line on the mainland is the Los Angeles River flood control channel; tiny fingers reaching into the sea left of it are the manmade San Pedro Harbor. The upper island is Santa Catalina, and the lower one is San Clemente. They are two of eight peaks of a mountain range under the Pacific. Santa Catalina is about 20 miles long and 8 miles wide.

122

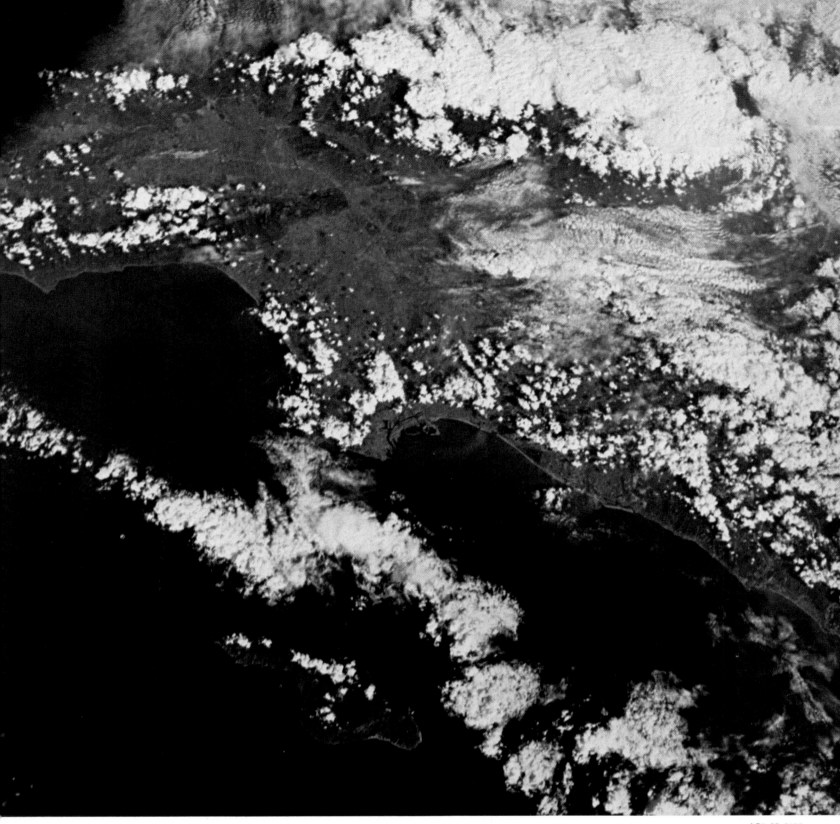

AS9-22-3436

Census analysts expect the population of the Los Angeles-Long Beach area shown here to be 10 million by 1975. The San Fernando Valley and the Santa Monica Mountains are in the upper left and the Peninsular Ranges are below the clouds at the right. Founded by Spaniards in 1781, Los Angeles has been a mecca for midwestern Americans throughout our century and now has the highest concentration of automobiles of any city in the world.

123

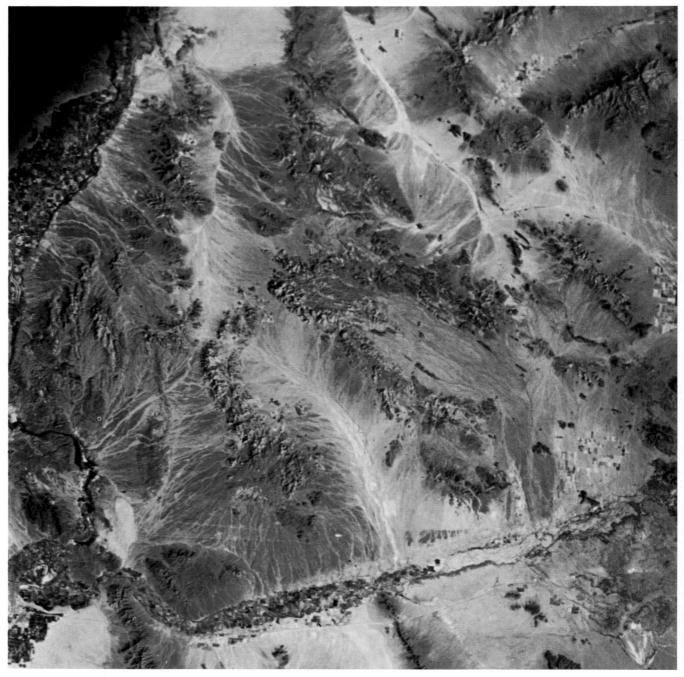

AS9-26A-3800

The Colorado River and Blythe, Calif., are in the upper left of this color infrared photo. Arizona's Dome Rock and Trigo Mountains are to the right of the river, and the Kofa Mountains and Castle Dome Peak are near the center of the view. Farmers' fields in the valley look tiny, pink, and square. Below the long strip of agricultural land on the Gila River in the foreground, faint straight lines indicate the course of the highway and the railway that run between Yuma and Gila Bend, Ariz.

124

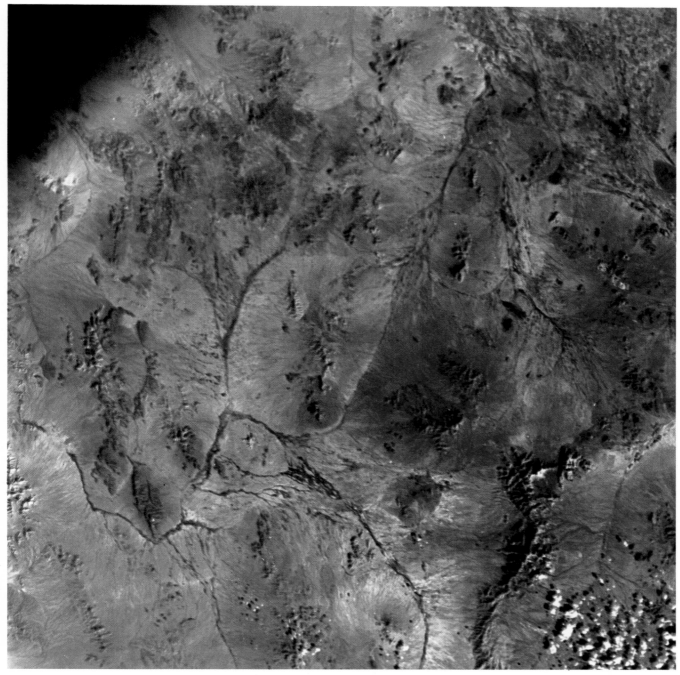

AS9-26A-3785A

Many of the dark areas in this image of southern Arizona and a sliver of northern Mexico are Tertiary volcanic rocks. A white blotch in the upper left is an open-pit copper mining area. "Nature's own cactus arboretum," the Organ Pipe Cactus National Monument, is below it. The cultivated fields in the upper right are near Tucson. The Sonoyta River is in the lower-left quadrant of the photo. Note, too, the mountain range in the lower right that resembles a seahorse; that is where the Kitt Peak National Observatory is located. It is a center for solar and planetary studies.

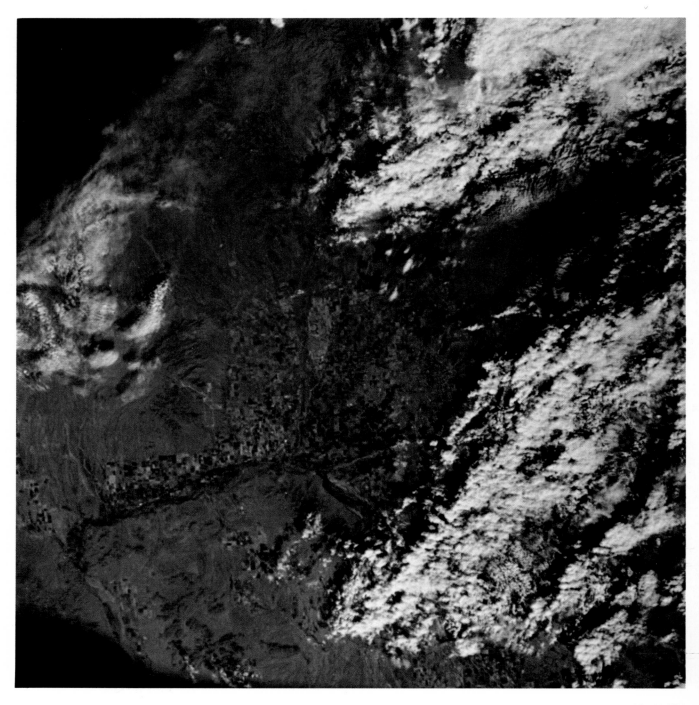

AS9-22-3441

The fields that look like a brown butterfly's speckled wings on the Earth's rough shell between the clouds here are in the environs of Phoenix, the capital and largest city in Arizona. The Gila River flows west from there to join the Colorado. Once the site of an Indian settlement, this modern city has benefited from rich mineral deposits nearby, large-scale irrigation of arid land, and the sunshine that has lured both vacationers and industry to the southwestern states.

126

AS9-20-3135

The Y-shaped reservoir here is Lake Mead. Its sharp western tip points toward a lightly hued area around the city of Las Vegas. The Colorado River carries water south across this part of the continent from the snow on the mountains of Utah and Colorado, and is the boundary here between Nevada and Arizona. Below Lake Mead is another reservoir. It is above Davis Dam, and below it there is a cultivated strip of land shaped like a mountain but distinguishable from one by its pattern.

AS9–20–3139

The Grand Canyon is in the upper left of this oblique view. In the center you see a great volcanic field, the San Francisco Peaks. A mere dot, to which the arrow on the right edge points, is the 4000-foot-wide Meteor Crater west of Winslow, Ariz. North America has many impact craters; this is the clearest one in the Apollo 9 photos.

The San Juan Mountains in Colorado are in the upper left and the Great Sand Dunes National Monument is in the upper center here. The Rio Grande flows through the valley in the foreground. The big circular feature left of the river is the 14-mile-wide Valles caldera, which somewhat resembles such lunar craters as Copernicus. Notice how elevation has governed the snow cover.

129

The strange, dark, two-legged figure that the clouds parted to reveal when an astronaut's camera looked west is the San Carlos Lake above the Coolidge Dam in eastern Arizona. No treasure like this water has been found on either the Moon or Mars. Some cultivation of the land can be noted along the Gila River. That river flows between the Piñaleno and the Gila Mountains, two volcanic and complex ranges that enclose alluvium-filled basins.

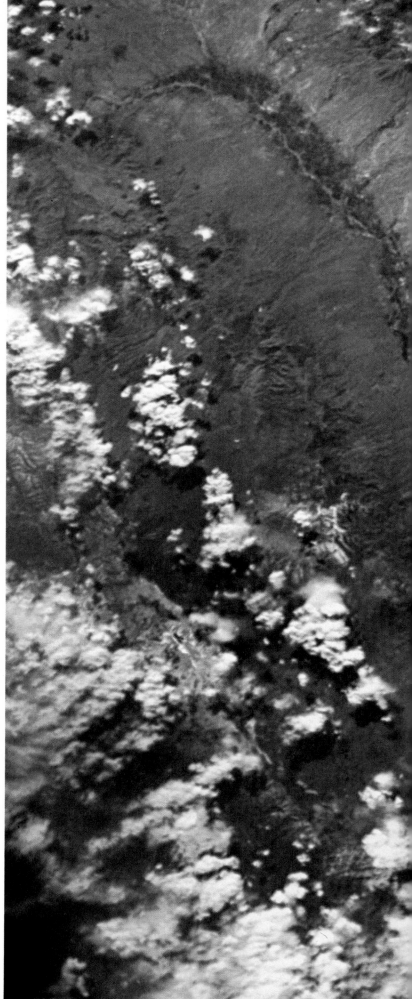

AS9–21–3291

AS9-26A-3803

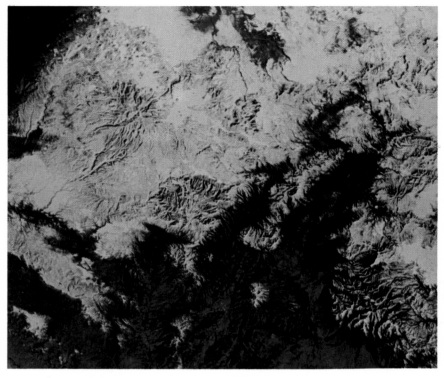

These are the White, Tularosa, and Gallo Mountains near Alpine, Ariz., and Luna, N. Mex. This is mainly a volcanic area, and the snow enhanced the view of fracture patterns in this color infrared photo. The dark-blue areas are vegetation.

Snow gave the infrared photo below the whiteness on the mountains west of the Rio Grande in New Mexico. The river is at the right. Elephant Butte and Caballo Reservoirs are in the lower right. Snow surveys help in managing the flow of rivers.

AS9-26A-3804

Arizona, Utah, Colorado, and New Mexico meet in the upper left corner of this picture, and Wyoming and Nebraska are on the horizon. The Rio Grande Valley winds diagonally from the left edge to the top of the view. Santa Fe is between it and the snow in the foreground. A dark circular tower with an inner ring to the right of the center is Turkey Mountain, 8500 feet high. The Park Plateau is above it, and Pikes Peak and Denver are farther north. The Capitan Mountains are in the lower left.

AS9–20–3122

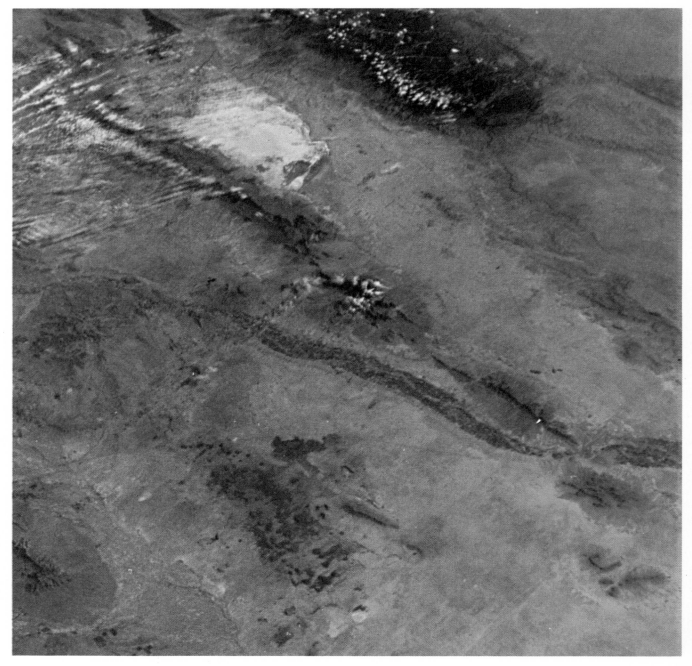

AS9-21-3282

The White Sands National Monument is in the upper center, above the San Andres Mountains, in this photo. The "white sands" are gypsum, carried into the basin by rains and snows, and supplemented by more material brought to the surface from thick beds underground. This whole area is believed to have once been a plateau. The river in the upper left is the Rio Grande. At El Paso, Tex., near the right edge, it becomes the boundary between the United States and Mexico.

134

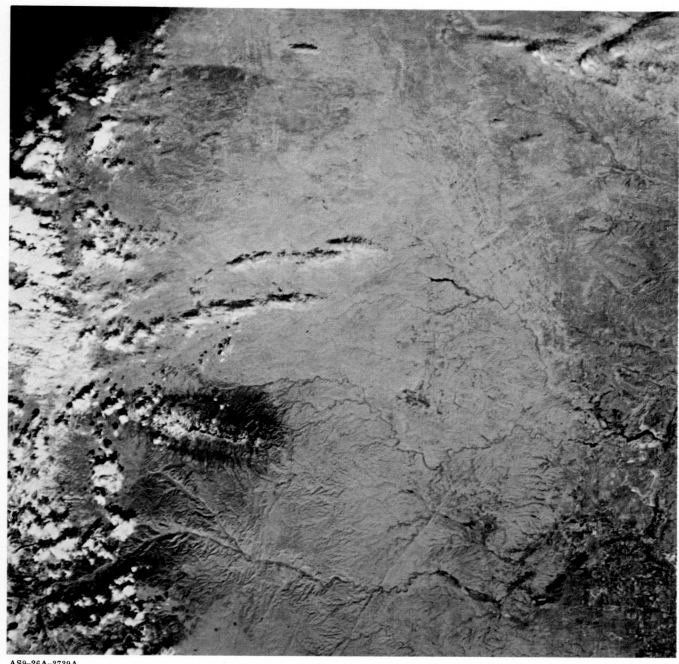

AS9-26A-3739A

When seen in a color infrared picture, Capitan Peak, west of Roswell, N. Mex. (in the lower left corner), looks like a brown insect scurrying for cover, even though it is 10 083 feet high. The snow on the mountain is barely distinguishable from the clouds. The Rio Hondo is in the southern part of the view and the vegetation along it looks slightly reddish here. The nearly straight, slanting line that crosses the river is an extension of a fault.

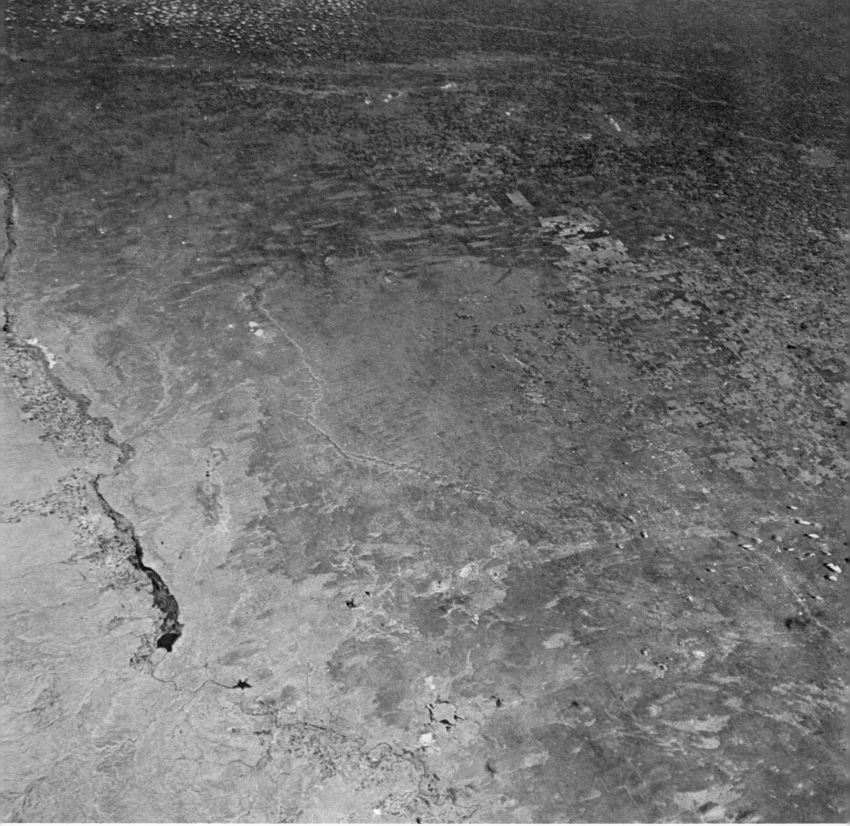

AS9-22-3332

The Pecos River wiggles down at the left to broaden above the Red Bluff Dam above Pecos, Tex. A well-defined line to the right of the river is the western edge of the Great Plains. The gray expanse in the center is an area in which the vegetation is mostly scrub. Beyond it to the right are the farmlands of the Texas Panhandle. In the upper right, the view extends into Oklahoma.

136

relatively young mountain systems, having resulted from an uplift in Late Cretaceous and Early Tertiary time, only about 70 million years ago. Rivers from their snowfields have remorselessly carved them ever since, and very recently men have been spreading their waters over fertile fields between the mountains. Sometimes slowly, and sometimes quite suddenly, natural and human forces have changed the appearance of the Western Cordillera.

A stranger to the continent, approaching the United States from the Pacific sky, might well decide to look elsewhere for a smooth place to set his vehicle down. The Southwestern States, nevertheless, are among the most beautiful parts of our continent. Their historic areas, great forests, and national parks can be seen now from higher vantage points than mountain climbers can reach or aircraft can fly to, yet motorists whose vacation trips have acquainted them with "ground truth" can easily recognize landmarks in the Apollo astronauts' pictures.

From the Mountains to the Prairies

Halfway between the Pacific and the Atlantic, Texas has more parts than Caesar's Gaul. Space photography shows how:

(1) The Rocky Mountains reach into its western tip south of New Mexico.

(2) The Great Plains east of the mountains run down its northern panhandle.

(3) A rugged limestone tableland separates these plains from the southern end of the continent's North Central Plains.

(4) The North Central Plains penetrate deep into the State's heart; and

(5) Gulf Coastal Plains spread inland from 50 to 300 miles along the Gulf of Mexico.

A Texan, of course, can add many et ceteras to any enumeration of the State's features—including dense thickets near the shore east of Houston, and the Manned Spacecraft Center on that city's edge. "Texas stands in the physical path of a special destiny," the historian Walter Prescott Webb wrote.

Although the flat landscape might be a welcome sight to an explorer looking for a place to entrust himself to the Earth's gravity, it was a disappointment to the first Europeans to see it. The Spaniards prowled along the northern rim of the Gulf in the 1500's, but found no gold, and did not bother to establish missions on the windy plains of Texas until a century later. Storms sweep into the Coastal Plain from the Gulf of Mexico at times. "I sat down and cried," the husky mayor of one Texas town said when asked what he did after one of those storms in 1970. Sandbars and shallow lagoons line most of the State's 600-plus miles of seacoast. Most of the harbors now in use were dredged out by men, and Houston did not begin to rival New Orleans as an international port until its canal to the sea was opened.

The flags of Spain, France, and Mexico, as well as the Lone Star, the Stars and Bars, and the Stars and Stripes, have flown over this State. Its wide-open spaces were used primarily for ranching, however, until the discovery of the oilfields in our century. Dry-farming techniques and irrigation have also increased the State's wealth, and new cities now sprawl over the plains.

While still over Texas, the astronauts began to see the broad lower portion of the world's greatest river system. Together the Mississippi and Missouri Rivers are about 4200 miles long and drain nearly a million and a quarter square miles of the continent. Fifty thousand or so years ago an inland sea apparently covered the fertile prairies of the Central States. Aided by the Ohio, the Red, and many other tributaries, the Mississippi lapped at the Ozark barrier to open an artery to the Gulf of Mexico. This channel drained that ancient sea, created vast flood plains as it wound its way hither and thither in response to gravity, and extended the continent farther south. Louisiana plantation owners found the soil immensely fertile when drained, and cotton, rice, citrus fruits, and beef cattle have all contributed to the development of the land along the Gulf.

For scores of years, the Mississippi River was the most important single objective of American military strategy. Ever since its shores were settled, civil engineers have been busy dredging, diking, and damming the continually changing channels of this natural drainage system. "Of all the eluding and ungraspable objects that ever I tried to get my hands on," Mark Twain wrote of the Mississippi's shape in the 1800's, "that was the chief."

Near Vicksburg, Miss., the Army built a big model of the Midwest in the 1940's to learn more about the continent's colossal drainage system. One

137

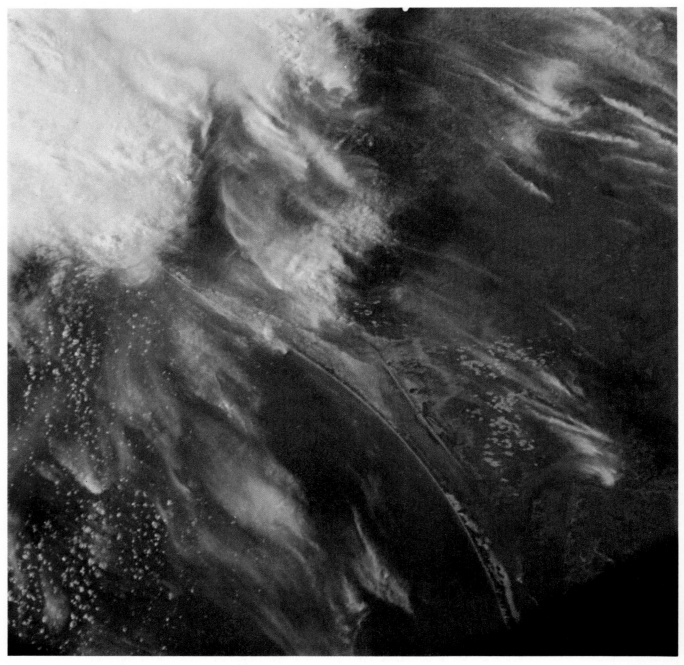

AS9–22–3407

Padre Island extends for 100 miles along the western edge of the Gulf of Mexico. This nearly vertical view of it south of Corpus Christi was recorded on a day when altostratus and cirrus uncinus clouds raced along the coastal plains. The Intracoastal Waterway runs through the Laguna Madre between the island and the mainland. The farms visible are near Kingsville and Riviera, on the Alazan and Baffin Bays. The brownish spots are coastal sand. Texas has many small lakes, salt ponds, and manmade reservoirs. Photos of the State from space show a great variety of features.

138

AS9-23-3578

The rangelands and farmlands in the vicinity of Childress, southeast of Amarillo, seem to flow like a broad river between banks of clouds in this photograph. Most of the rivers of Texas head directly for the Gulf of Mexico, but in the northern part of the State they flow to the east. The Middle Pease and North Pease join here on their way to the Red River. Above them is Prairie Dog Town Fork. Deciduous shrub and forest stands line the rivers on relatively high parts of the sedimentary plateau in this part of the continent.

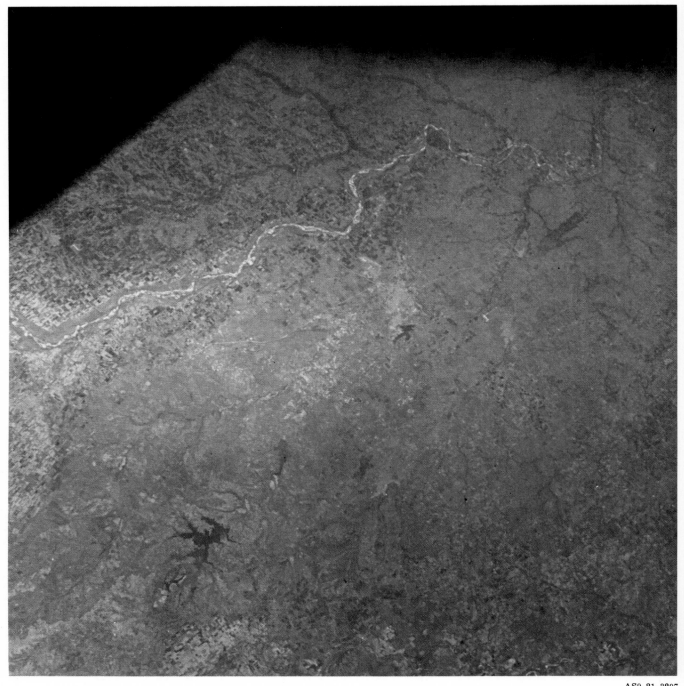

AS9-21-3297

The Red River in the upper half of this photo derived its name from the red clay through which it flows. Tremendous volumes of soil blew away from here during the drought in the 1930's. Lake Kemp and the Wichita River valley are in the lower left, and the city of Wichita Falls, Tex., is near the center of this vertical view. For part of the Red River's course to the Mississippi, it is the boundary between Texas and Oklahoma.

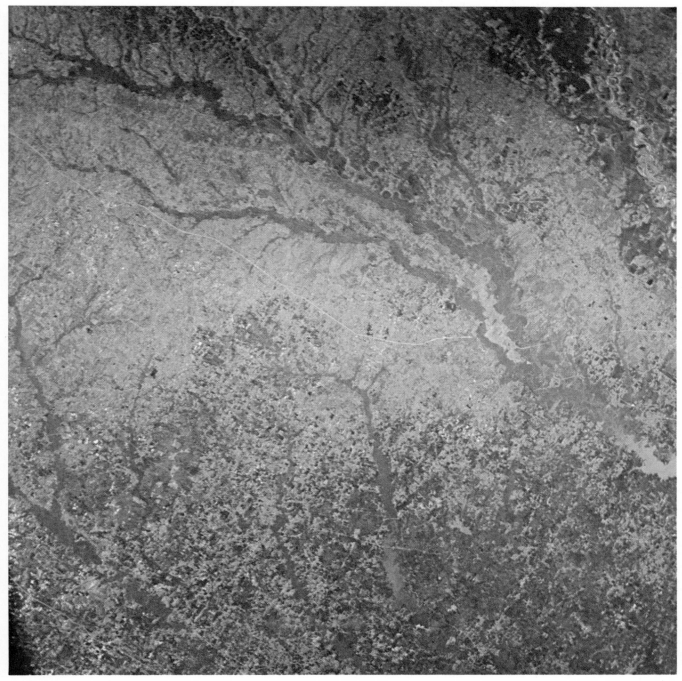

AS9–21–3300

The drainage system gives this photo taken over northern Texas its pattern. The two prominent dark lines from the upper left that join toward the right are branches of the Sulphur River. The Trinity River valley is in the lower left, and that meandering stream in the upper right corner is the Red. Lake Texarkana is at the right edge, just below the center. That long, curveless light line across the photo is a road from Dallas to Texarkana, Ark.

141

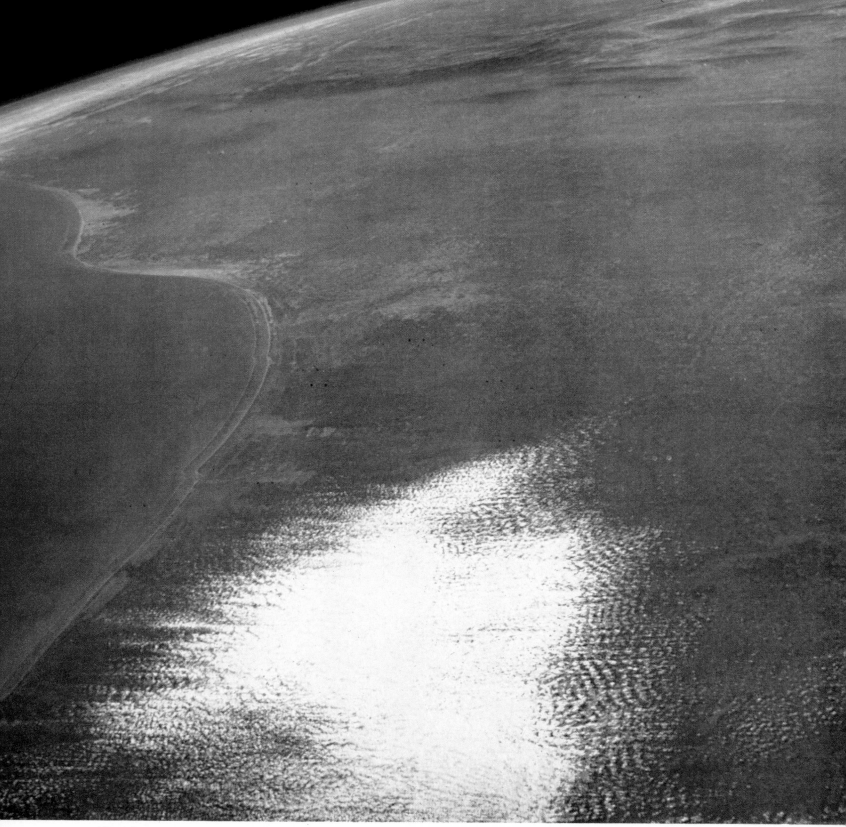

AS9-19-2990

The long oblique view at the left is from over Louisiana, and extends to Mexico. Near the center, cultivated areas can be noted between Matagorda Bay and Victoria, Tex. Corpus Christi is on a large bay toward the upper left. Near the horizon, the Rio Grande flows past Brownsville to the gulf. Its mouth is closer to the Equator than is that of the Nile. Oranges sometimes ripen in southern Texas while blizzards rage in the northern panhandle.

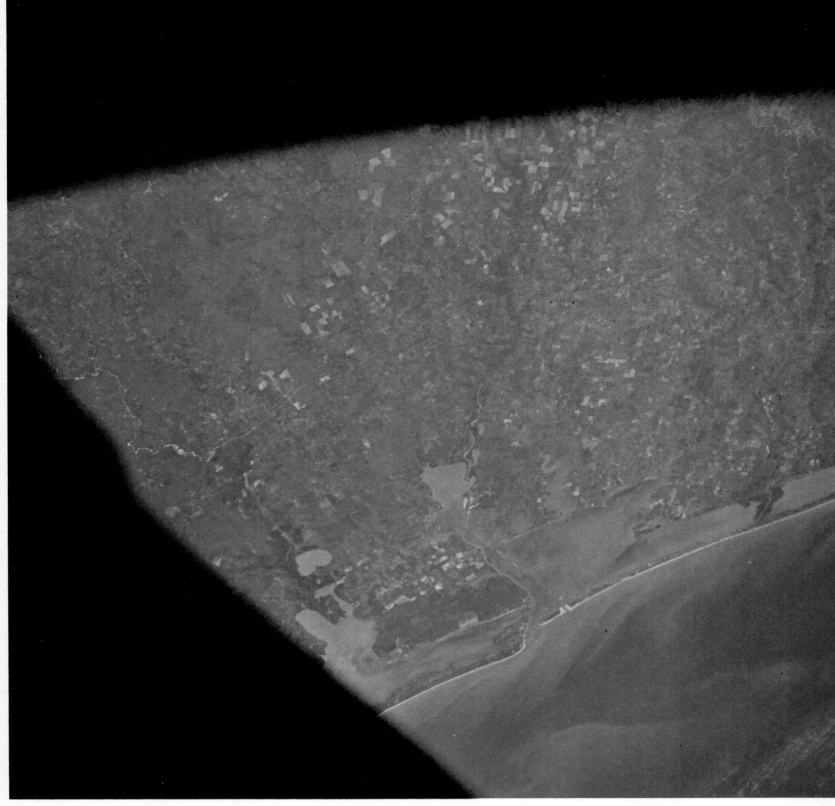

AS9–22–3342

In southern Texas, the rivers carry soil directly into the Gulf of Mexico. This is part of the coastal plain between Victoria and Matagorda Bay, southwest of Houston. North of the lagoons and sandbars along the coast, the land is now intensively cultivated. Below them a southerly longshore current was distributing sediment on the continental shelf the day that this picture was taken.

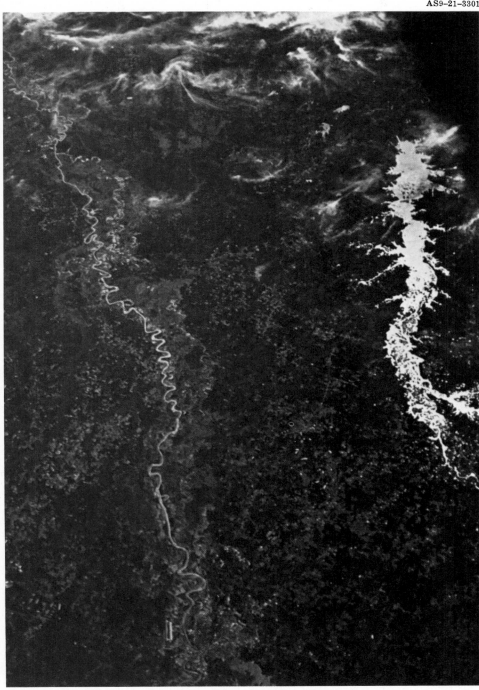

The view above is to the southeast. It shows the Red River valley in Louisiana between Shreveport and Natchitoches, an area well suited for farming. The long white figure is sun glitter from the Sabine River wetlands. Straight light marks in the foreground are Barksdale Air Force Base near Shreveport.

The large view at the left extends from Freeport, Tex., to Sabine Lake on the Louisiana boundary. Houston, the Nation's largest inland port and leading refining center, is at the upper end of Galveston Bay, that large indentation in the mainland. Woods darken the coastal plain of eastern Texas.

145

The camera was pointed south from high over the State of Mississippi to obtain this oblique view. In it the lower Mississippi River winds its way eastward after serving as a boundary between Louisiana and Mississippi. All of Lake Maurepas and a part of Lake Pontchartrain are also visible at the far left. Natchez, Miss., is about in the center of the right third of the picture (on this page). A relatively tiny stream, the Thompson River, flows south to join the big river near Baton Rouge, La. (There are other views of the Mississippi River in chs. 3 and 4.)

AS9–21–3303

of the test sites for the Apollo photographic experiment in 1969 was also near Vicksburg. There, overflowing streams and woodlands were examined alongside fields and cities. By checking those pictures with findings on the ground, foresters now are learning how to interpret space pictures of similar areas more quickly and accurately.

The Eastern Seaboard

North America's coastal plains extend east and north from the Mississippi Delta. Florida was once an island rather than a peninsula. The shoreline north of it as well as to the west has changed since the Appalachian Mountains emerged some 200 million years ago. Gracefully curving capes and sandbars similar to those on the Gulf's edge now frame much of the Atlantic Seaboard. Without ever landing on the continent, however, a space tourist could see remarkable differences between its eastern third and its central prairies.

The wrinkles in this part of the Earth's shell are much gentler than the western ranges, and vegetation rather than snow cloaks all but a few high points most of the year. Brooks burbling down the eastern slopes cross a fertile plateau before reaching the lowlands, and become broad, navigable streams as they approach the Atlantic. Natural harbors are plentiful on this coast, and winds from the west make it a lee shore.

This was the first part of the continent to feel an English hoe, but the settlers soon found that moving into the primeval forests that lined the rivers could be perilous. England's first colony, planted on an island off Virginia late in the 1500's, vanished without leaving a clue to its people's fate. To symbolize North America on the ceiling of the Bishop's Palace at Werzburg, in the early 1700's, Giovanni Battista Tiepolo, the greatest decorator of his time, portrayed a nearly nude Indian girl riding a crocodile.

The Spaniards, after searching in vain for a fountain of youth in Florida, clung to that peninsula and kept a long strip of the Gulf coast pointed like a rifle barrel at the Mississippi River's mouth. For two centuries, the colonists farther north found the Appalachians—which look so puny now from altitudes of a hundred or more miles—a challenging barrier to westward migration. But the land-hungry new nation created by 13 eastern colonies in their pursuit of happiness persisted in expanding both to the west and to the south, despite both the natural and the national obstacles. Men speed through the former wilderness today on concrete ribbons, sometimes pausing in the "Land of the Sky" to view the trees from lookout points.

Most of the gold produced in the United States came from the Appalachians until 1849. We do not now think of the East as rich in minerals, but 39 valuable ores and minerals have been found in various parts of Georgia. That State, the largest one east of the Mississippi, was the last of the 13 English colonies in America to be settled. Nearly every plant that thrives in our country can be grown in Georgia, and farming is the chief activity. Atlanta, the capital, has become the financial, air-traffic, and distribution hub of the whole Southeast.

The first settlers in South Carolina found few lakes there, but the land was richly productive. When Charleston was establishing its reputation as a center of the old South, people often said it was the city "where the Ashley and Cooper Rivers meet to form the Atlantic Ocean." Space pictures suggest still how true that quip must have seemed to children confined to the New World. Yet the same pictures also show several large bodies of water inland, created as reservoirs, and an Atlantic Intercoastal Waterway between the islands and the mainland.

Canadian geese and other waterfowl still refresh themselves on the capes off North Carolina before continuing their long flights north and south, but men have put these sandy shoals to an astonishing variety of uses that their discoverers could not foresee. The pirate Blackbeard hid out and died on one of those capes. R. A. Fessenden, whose studies helped make today's radio-communication systems possible, conducted his experiments on a Carolina cape. More recently, the Wright Brothers, aided by a half-dozen men from a lifesaving station, lugged their 605-pound airplane up a slope at Kitty Hawk, and after several trials got it airborne.

In the Apollo 9 pictures, the sands where the air age began look little, if any, different now than they must have a half century ago. But the Florida cape from which the first men to go to the Moon left North America has an utterly different kind of beauty now than it once did. Both capes are works of nature now memorable because of what men did there.

148

Looking northeast from Birmingham, one sees snow on the Appalachian Mountains all the way to Virginia, West Virginia, and Pennsylvania. The mountain chain begins with the Smokies in the lower left and runs diagonally to the horizon. Some geologists consider this the best space picture of this region obtained thus far. Atlanta, Chattanooga, Asheville, and Knoxville are among the area's cities. A small orange spot in the left center is dead vegetation where copper has been smelted near Ducktown, Tenn.

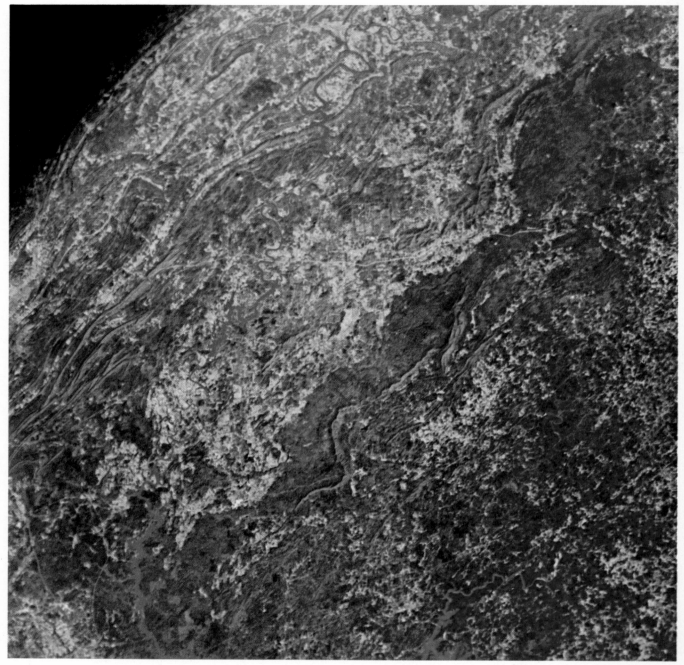

AS9–26A–3790A

The Alabama Geological Survey used this color infrared photo in studies of ground water. The bright-blue line that zigzags down it is the Coosa River between Birmingham and Anniston, Ala. The blue patch in the lower right is Martin Lake. The highest point in Alabama is on the Cumberland Plateau, east of the Coosa and north of the lake. Great compressive forces within the Earth long ago produced the narrow folds of the Appalachian Mountains. Now etched by erosion, those folds stand out clearly in this photograph.

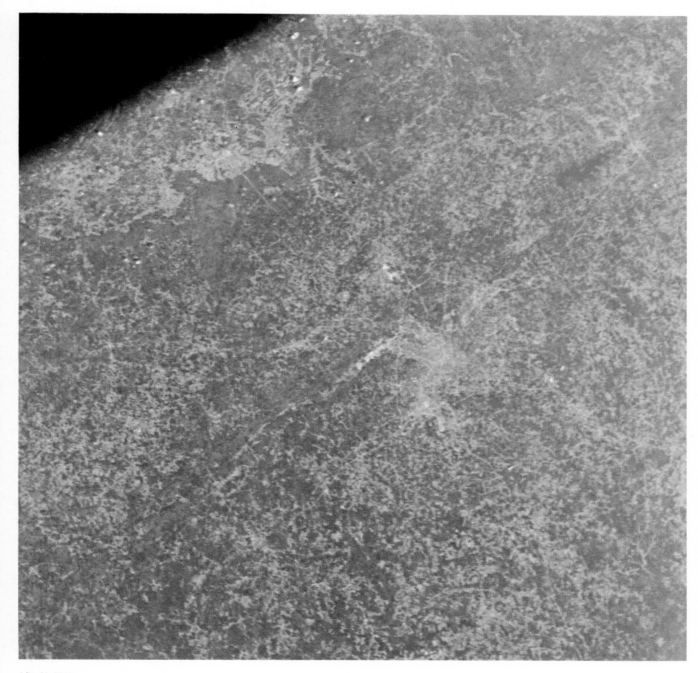

AS9-23-3567

The faint lines that resemble a spider web on the landscape here are around Atlanta, Georgia's largest city. A piedmont plateau of rolling foothills extends past the city from the mountains about 50 miles north of it. Lake Sidney Lanier is in the upper right corner of this view. Atlanta is 1050 feet above sea level, and is on the Brevard fault zone that is discernible, when this photo is examined closely, as a dark band from the lower left to the upper right. The small white dots in the upper left are scattered cumulus.

This is Florida's west coast. Tampa Bay is in the lower center. St. Petersburg is on the peninsula above the entrance to it. Bridges that serve that city and Tampa are visible. The river below Tampa Bay is the Manatee, and Sarasota Bay is below it. The average elevation of the land in Florida is only about 100 feet, and the large bays on the west coast were formed by the sinking of river valleys long ago. The hues of the Gulf water here suggest the extent of the continental shelf.

152 Florida's east coast is at the right. Cape Kennedy is just below the center of the photo. Tiny spots connected by roads on the cape are launching pads. At the inland end of the bridges to the cape, buildings along the highway lighten the view. The sands of Daytona Beach are north of the spaceport. Gemini astronauts' pictures of this area showed changes in the transportation network that were not indicated yet in the roadmaps. This is where all of NASA's manned space flights have started.

AS9-26A-3816A

Three-fifths of Georgia is coastal flatland. This infrared photo shows the southernmost part of it. The St. Marys River, Florida's northern boundary, is at the bottom edge of the picture. The city of Brunswick is nearly in the center. The shoreline shown extends from Cumberland Island to Ossabaw Island. Emerged beach ridges are visible in the lower left. Highways here run through mixed pine and hardwood forests to link scattered cultivated areas. There are some pure stands of both pine and hardwood.

154

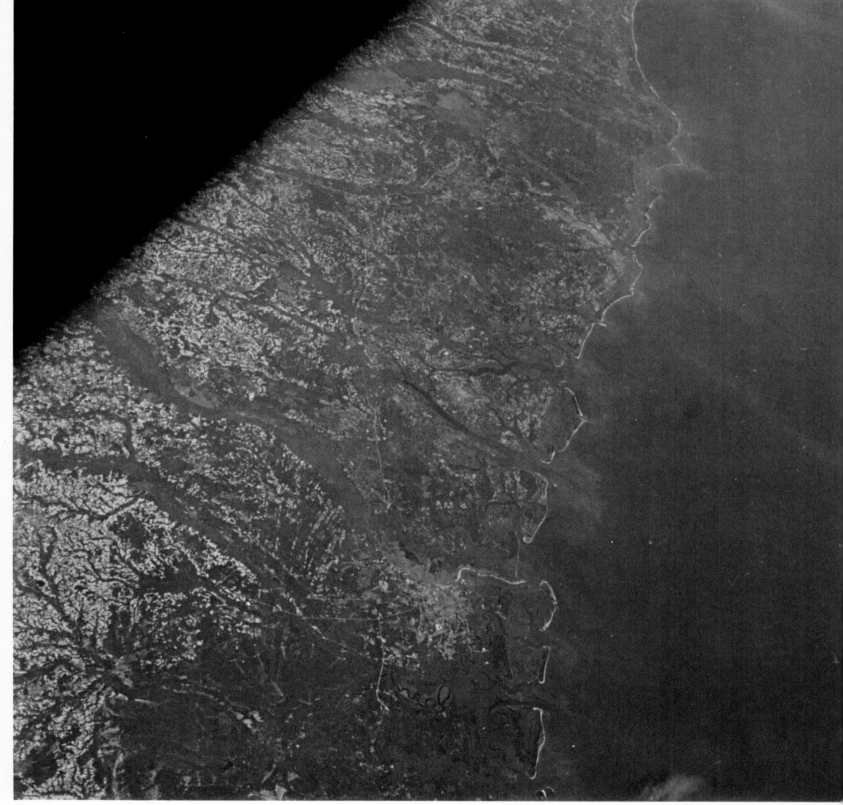

AS9-20-3148

The eastern seaboard's offshore islands become narrower north of Georgia. The Savannah River, South Carolina's southern boundary, is near the bottom of this picture, and the city of Savannah is in a light area nearby. From there the oblique view extends northeast past Charleston to Myrtle Beach. Hence it shows nearly the whole shoreline of South Carolina. Sediment patterns from streams flowing into the Atlantic Ocean reveal shore currents, and can help engineers anticipate beach erosion.

AS9-23-3568

Charleston, one of America's oldest and most famous cities, is nearly in the center of this view of the South Carolina coast. The Fort Sumter National Monument is at the entrance to its harbor. Folly Beach is below the city. Port Royal Sound, in the lower left corner, and Bulls Bay, at the upper right, are both recognizable by their shapes and the sedimentation in the water. Lake Moultrie is near the center of the top edge of the picture.

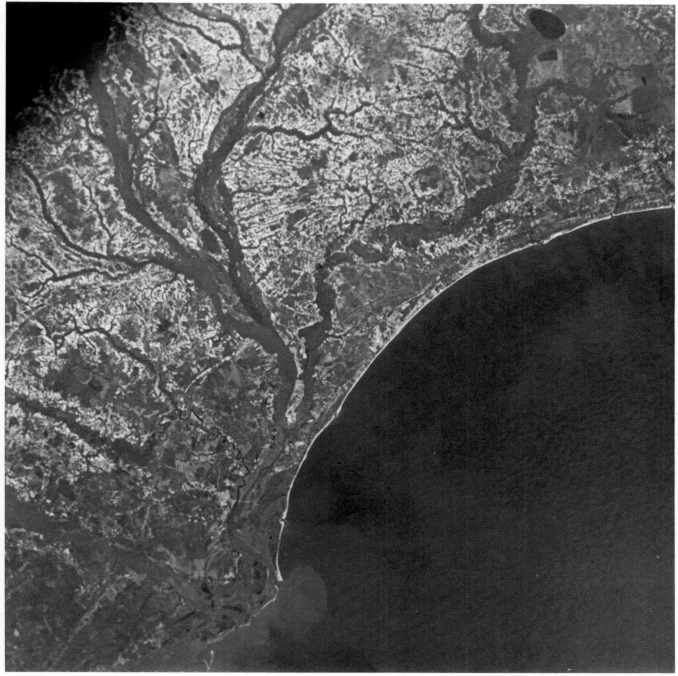

AS9-26A-3793A

Rivers born in Appalachian forests become placidly mature by the time they reach the Carolina shore. The Santee's mouth is in the lower left of this color infrared photo, and the Pee Dee's mouth is above it. Myrtle Beach curves to the east at the right. The Atlantic Intercoastal Waterway runs between it and the mainland down toward Winyah Bay at the Santee's mouth. The blue oval in the upper right is Lake Waccamaw in North Carolina.

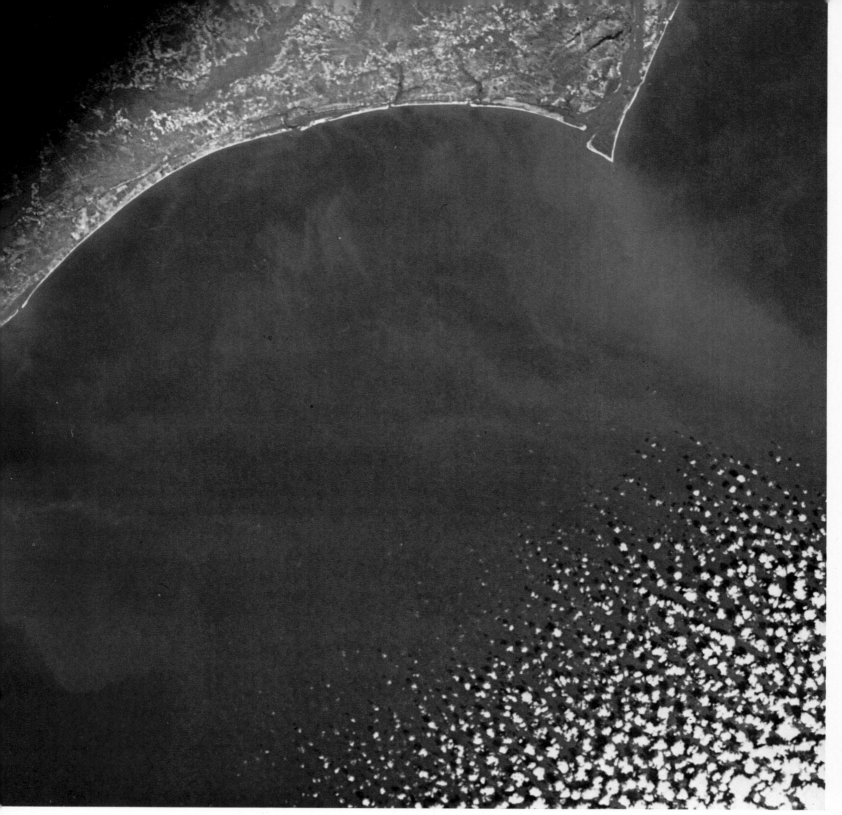

AS9-26A-3776A

The white hook pointed toward the altocumulus clouds over the Atlantic in this color infrared photo is North Carolina's Cape Fear. The distribution of the sediment indicates that a northeasterly current was flowing off Myrtle Beach when this picture was taken. Most rivers in this vicinity enter sounds, but the Cape Fear River flows right to the ocean. Spaniards from Santo Domingo established a colony briefly here in the early 1500's. Two centuries later, Europeans rapidly settled the Cape Fear River valley.

158

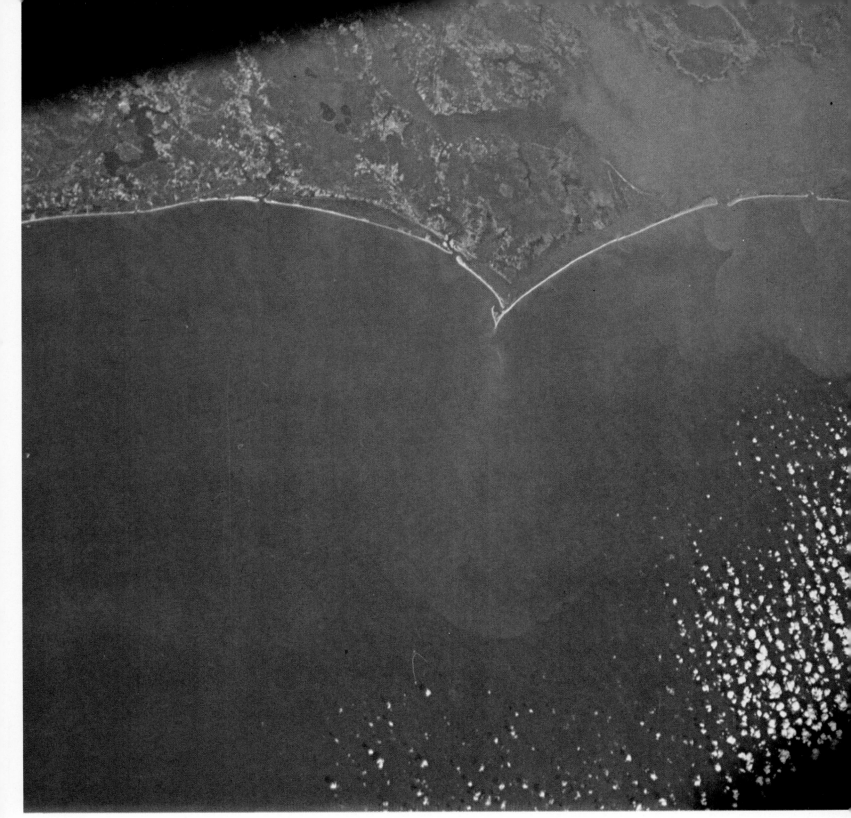

AS9-20-3127

This is how Cape Lookout, N.C., looks from almost directly above it in space. Morehead City and Onslow Bay are to the left of its sharp tip, and Raleigh Bay is to the right. Notice how the fine plume of sediment leaving the cape's end seems to blossom out over the continental shelf of the ocean. The Neuse River flows into Pamlico Sound, which is in the upper right here, and sediment bulges out to the sea through sandy shoals there. There is much marshland and farming in this coastal region.

AS9-20-3128

Cape Hatteras is almost in the center of this view of narrow coastal islands. Shoals here have long imperiled seamen, and in this picture even the clouds seem to be avoiding the sediment that is changing the ocean's hue near them. To the left above Hatteras is Albemarle Sound, and to the left below it are Pamlico Sound and Cape Lookout. The Wright Brothers National Monument is at Kitty Hawk, between Albemarle Sound and the Atlantic.

161

On a clear March day, from high over the Carolinas, the Atlantic shore was visible to New York City and Long Island, and one could almost see spring advancing to the north. Virginia Beach is in the left foreground of the photo at the left. Snow lay over parts of Delaware and New Jersey, and there were clouds on the northern horizon. But the threads of cumulus over the ocean simply pointed to the Chesapeake and Delaware Bays, and Capes Henry, Charles, Henlopen, and May, leaving them exposed.

AS9-20-3129

BEAUFORT SEA →

LAKE WINNIPEG →

SALT LAKE ⟶

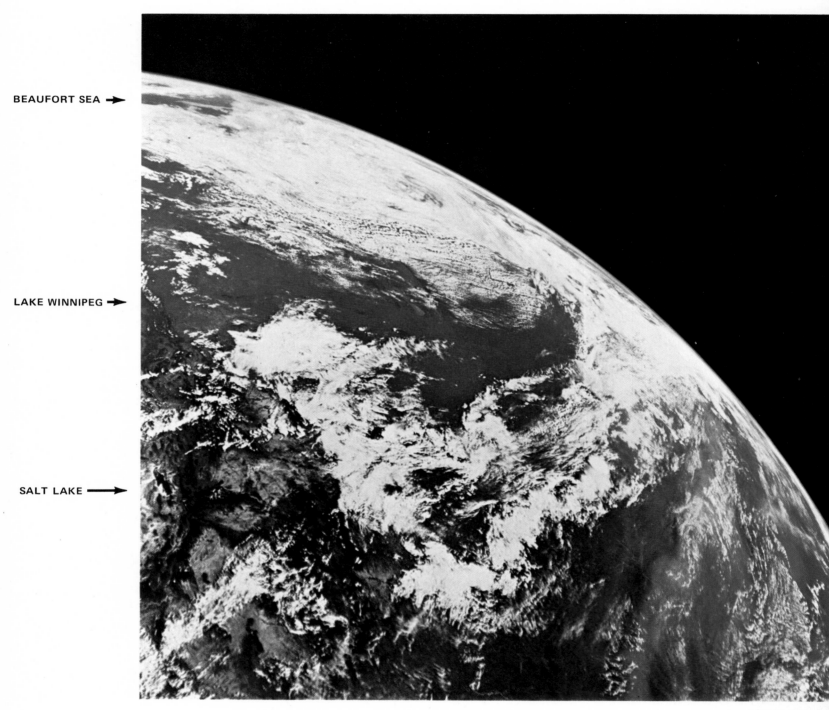

AS11-36-5307

The Apollo 11 crew looked back on the way to the Moon and took this photo. The view extends across our mountains and plains from the desert west of Salt Lake, at the far left, to clouds over the land that outlined Chesapeake Bay and Cape Hatteras at the right. Canada's northern boundary, the Beaufort Sea, is visible at the left near the horizon.

162

7

Beyond This Island Earth

We shall always go a little further . . .
Beyond that last blue mountain barred with snow
Across that angry or that glimmering sea
—JAMES ELROY FLECKER

NATURAL FORCES drive us forward. When not deflected by circumstances, men have always done what they could to advance the science of their day. Since prehistory, the exploration of space has been a continuing effort, begun when man had only his eyes and mind to work with. These were powerful tools, as evidenced by the calendars and eclipse predictions of ancient peoples, by the astronomical awareness implicit in the design of Stonehenge, and by Eratosthenes' brilliant calculation around 240 B.C. of the probable circumference of the Earth. (He deduced it from comparative Sun angles at noon on one particular day in Syene and in Alexandria, and achieved a very respectable accuracy.)

In the 17th, 18th, and 19th centuries, the telescope, chronometer, spectroscope, and photographic plate greatly enlarged our ability to observe and measure. The new technology made a period of wonderful advances possible in planetary astronomy. It was unmatched until the present. Early in this century, astronomy of the solar system came upon several decades of doldrums. The instrumental harvest, in the main, had apparently been reaped; the exciting discoveries had seemingly already been made; and the remote abstractions of astrophysics became more intellectually fashionable.

Today, not solely because of our new ability in space, the situation has swung dramatically around. Young scientists—the presence of bright youngsters is a sensitive indicator of the promise in a particular field—are flocking to planetary work. Men and women not initially trained in astronomy—geo-physicists and geologists, meteorologists and atmospheric chemists, biologists, and experts in the new fields of radio and radar astronomy—are all joining in the exploration of the numerous new vistas opening up in solar-system science.

New instruments are being devised that provide significantly better data. Spectroscopes based on interferometry principles, to select one example, now provide planetary spectra of greatly improved resolution in the infrared band of the spectrum. Some of this complex new gear, delicate and troublesome even in an observatory workroom, is now being experimentally carried up toward the top of the filtering atmosphere in jet-plane laboratories, with results that richly repay the patience and skill required. There is excitement over the fact that the turbulent, vapor-clouded window that heretofore has given astronomy its only view outside will, in effect, be entirely avoided. Precursor spacecraft like the Orbiting Solar and Astronomical Observatories have already given us fascinating glimpses of the ultraviolet-rich universe.

The new subdisciplines of radio and radar astronomy have begun, in the classic patterns of scientific advance, to cast fresh light on older problems while at the same time illuminating altogether new ones. It is technically exciting, for example, to use radar to establish the 243-day axial rotation of cloud-shrouded Venus, but quite another thing to understand how under the heavens this Earth-synchronized rotation can have come about. It is fascinating to discover that Jupiter is (after the

163

Sun) the most powerful emitter of radio energy in the solar system, but baffling to find that some of its bursts of radio noise, for inexplicable reasons, correlate with the position of its satellite Io. It is provocative to detect in the interstellar medium abundant oxygen-hydrogen molecules as well as such other substances as carbon monoxide, water, ammonia, and formaldehyde, but for the moment it is quite beyond us to comprehend how a cold gas cloud can generate maser energies. We learn more, and learn there is more to learn.

We can now foresee the logic that will almost certainly shape the next decade of planetary exploration. The method will be different from the way in which the Earth itself was explored. On its surface, men moved out from known localities, as means of travel and survival permitted, in random forays beyond the perimeter of the known. In space we will not have analogs of the Phoenicians or Norsemen, restless peoples driven by obscure restless motives, nor equivalents to Marco Polo and Vasco da Gama, individualists who bravely pursued their often-innocent objectives. Instead, we will explore space on a rational foundation of what is already known.

Exploring by Machine

We will begin—we have in fact already begun—by using automated exploring machines of great technical virtuosity. Men will follow them to the planets only when the potential reward for manning our spacecraft is clearly warranted, justifying the humanistic requirement for a confidently safe two-way trip.

The expendable robot explorers may be divided into distinct classes according to types of mission. The first is the flyby probe, relatively the simplest to design, launch, and control, although only relatively so. While this type of spacecraft may be asked to report on conditions sensed during its long cruise through interplanetary space, its prime reason is to send back an intensive burst of data as it moves past close to the target planet, when multiple sensors report on the encounter with a new world. Once its work is done and reported, the flyby probe typically bends off into solar orbit, where it remains indefinitely, silently, a manmade asteroid.

The second class of automated spacecraft is the orbiter, which is both more demanding technically

and more rewarding scientifically. There are several reasons for the improved return of data from it. One is that, if injected into a highly inclined orbit, the spacecraft can instrumentally scan the entire surface of the planet rotating beneath it. The second is that, if all goes well, the orbiter will operate on station long enough to record the temporal or seasonal changes that may take place, such as the recurrent wave of darkening on Mars.

The next class of automatic explorer is a spacecraft fitted with atmospheric probes that are discharged to descend to the surface, telemetering back data on the pressure, temperature, and composition of the gases through which the probes pass. Such probes can offer us an instructive profile of the atmosphere, and permit correlation with measurements already made from Earth or from orbit. The only ones known to have been flown at this writing were three Russian devices introduced into the dense atmosphere of Venus.

The last class of spacecraft in this series is a combination of an orbiter, entry probe, and softlander, the latter instrumented to report on conditions prevailing on the surface. The orbiter serves as more than just a carrier spacecraft; it also acts as a radio relay, collecting data at each pass over the lander and sending it back to Earth at the appropriate time. Three of these four categories of exploring machines rely on information provided by the kind that preceded it. The flyby probe helps in the design of the orbiter, which in turn surveys the whole planet, helping in the selection of landing sites; and the atmospheric probe is important in engineering a lander that can decelerate and come to rest on the surface in working condition.

Something New Under the Sun

These unmanned spacecraft are truly something new under the Sun. They are robots that we have just barely learned to design, launch, and control. A generation ago, experienced engineers would almost certainly have believed that such mechanisms could not be made to work, and at that time they would have been right. Technologically, interplanetary spacecraft require a level of engineering sophistication that makes an automobile equivalent to a flint ax.

Consider the problem: produce a compact, lightweight, and exceptionally reliable mechanism that

JET PROPULSION LABORATORY

This gleaming object is Mariner 7, which flew by within 2100 miles of Mars in 1969. It sent more than a hundred pictures and a large amount of scientific data back to Earth 50 million miles away. It is now an artificial planetoid, in solar orbit.

can be folded up atop a stack of rockets and then hurled abruptly off the Earth at a precise time, undergoing a vibrating, high-G acceleration maintained until the robot achieves a velocity in excess of 7 miles a second in a precise direction in space. Give it an onboard electrical power system, using solar cells if the destination is a region where solar energy will be adequate, or a radioisotope thermoelectric generator if the Sun will be too distant. (Encase the latter so securely as to guarantee its integrity if the launch vehicle should fail.) Remember that during launch the robot will pass through a low-pressure region where destructive high-voltage arcing can occur. Remember also that the machine will spend its entire working lifetime in a vacuum so high that entrapped gases bubble out

of many normally inert composites and materials.

Design your spacecraft so that bulky appendages, such as solar-cell arrays, high-gain antennas, and magnetically sensitive instruments on booms, can be automatically unfolded and locked in precise positions after the shroud—needed to protect the machine during its passage through the atmosphere—falls away. Build into the robot an orientation system that will position it properly in an environment where there is no up or down, and no horizon, using Sun and star sensors in perpendicular planes that automatically operate small jets of cold gas, stored aboard in high-pressure flasks. Also provide a precisely controllable, self-igniting onboard rocket of substantial thrust, to refine the trajectory of the spacecraft so that it will pass through a needle's-

165

eye spot in space months ahead, when the path of the planet will bring that target to the rendezvous. Arrange matters so that you can temporarily disable the orientation system, turning the spacecraft into a remotely selected, gyro-established attitude, holding it there for the seconds and fractions of seconds that the course-correcting rocket is remotely burned, and then returning your robot to its Sun-locked, star-locked cruise position.

Devise an automatic temperature-control system for various parts of your spacecraft, keeping all thermally sensitive devices within a survivable band between intense solar heat and frigid shadowed cold. Provide a two-way radio link with Earth that, while consuming less watts than an ordinary light bulb, can reliably communicate for many months over hundreds of millions of miles. If the geometry of the mission calls for it, arrange for the high-gain antenna to be redirected periodically to aim it accurately at Earth. Build into your machine scores of sensors of temperature, pressure, position, voltage, current, acceleration, and events, funneling their messages into the communication system in quick bursts so that watchful men on the planet Earth can keep abreast of how the spacecraft is performing.

Carry along an onboard computer and sequencer to act as a brain for the robot. Load its memory with stored commands that will be issued automatically at the proper time and order, in case there is a partial malfunction that interferes with direct command, or in case the distance is so great that direct commands would take too long in transit. But hedge your bets by designing the brain so that new orders and sequences can also be inserted by Earth command.

As the sole reason for all this subtle and intricate engineering, select a scientific payload that will detect and measure physical characteristics of the planet or planets being surveyed. Choose a group of mutually complementary, noninterfering, scientifically significant experiments that will transmit back coded, meaningful, but possibly unexpected data. Mount the scientific sensors on a scan platform that can be commanded to tilt and slew to provide full coverage of the area scanned.

When, as during a planetary flyby, data are collected at a rate that would swamp the telecommunications link, provide a complete information-storage system for playback to Earth later at a slower rate. Design, build, test, and launch your spacecraft

against a timetable rigidly established by the movement of the planets. To prevent accidental seeding elsewhere of terrestrial organisms, construct, test, and launch your robot under conditions of strictly maintained sterility, picking your way cautiously past the dilemma that sterilization of electronic parts may affect their performance or reliability.

Finally support your vehicles with a 24-hour, worldwide guidance-and-command system. Provide giant dish antennas at stations located around the Earth, complete with powerful transmitters and supersensitive receivers, banks of high-speed computers, emergency power supplies, redundant communication and data networks. Organize several hundred people into smooth-running special teams concerned with trajectory analysis, engineering status, emergency planning, and the control and calibration of the scientific gear onboard. Rehearse the teams both intensively and imaginatively, to allay your anxieties lest a single blunder under pressure ruin the entire multi-million-dollar mission and hundreds of man-years of work.

After some disheartening but in the main instructive failures, the United States has performed this improbable feat 13 times for the Moon, twice for Venus, and three times for Mars. The result has been an unprecedented yield of otherwise unobtainable information.

How Little We Knew

In a time of an avalanche of new knowledge, it is easy to forget how recently we knew so little. It was only a little more than a decade ago, when the first artificial satellites began to circle Earth, that we knew for sure how radio communications would work in space, that moving parts would not coldweld into rigidity, that mechanisms would not be speedily disabled by radiation or micrometeorites. The 1960's were well begun before we knew for certain that human beings could be sent into space, to observe, work, and—specific for the species—think, and then be brought back unimpaired to the surface of our planet.

It was as recently as 1966 that Surveyor 1—a robot that, on its first flight, flawlessly made a radar-controlled landing on another body in the solar system, and turned on its television eye to stare about with the insatiable curiosity of its creators—showed that men setting foot on the Moon

Two years and seven months after the unmanned spacecraft Surveyor 3 came to rest in a shallow crater on the Moon, it was joined by the Apollo 12 lunar module, shown on the rim. Some Surveyor parts were brought back to Earth in working condition.

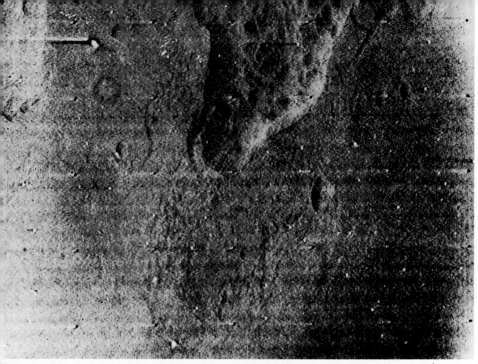

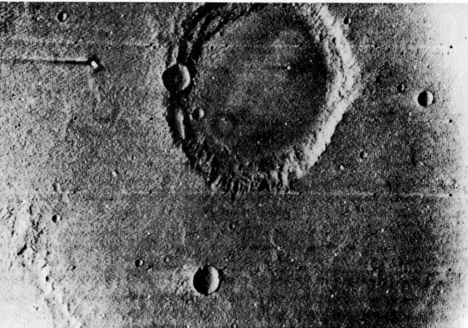

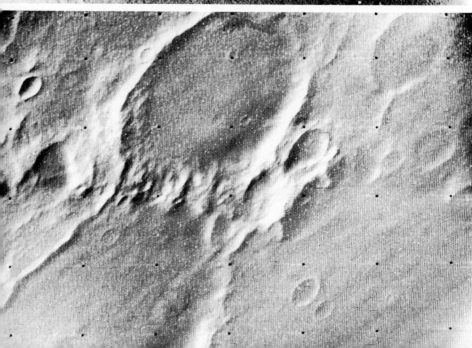

Three views of Mars are at the left, taken by flyby spacecraft in 1969. At the top is slumped, chaotic terrain of a type not found on the Moon, nor on the Earth in such extensive areas. In the middle is cratered terrain. The large crater with slump terraces on its walls is approximately 24 miles across; the small crater to the right is comparable in size to Meteor Crater, Ariz. (See p. 173.) At bottom is the "Giant's Footprint," two craters foreshortened by oblique viewing. The area covered is about 85 by 200 miles.

would not sink in a quicksand of moondust. Since then we have learned that our expendable machines can be asked to perform tasks of remarkable delicacy, and that our astronauts can be sent off with higher confidence of safe return than the hardy sailors had who first crossed the unknown oceans. This is not to say that men enter space without risk; that is implicit in exploration. But the perils are surely no greater now than those faced by the men who fought through a marginally survivable environment a few decades ago to reach the Earth's poles.

Earth Orbit and Lunar Bases

Forecasting the future is a chancy thing, but we can nonetheless make out dim shapes of what may lie ahead. One obvious need is a launch-vehicle system that is not discarded after one use. Plans are underway for a reusable booster able to lift a large payload into Earth orbit, and then return home to fly another day. Such a transportation system will dramatically cut the cost of space operations, and permit us to repair or modify unmanned equipment already in orbit. It will also serve as a shuttle to and from orbiting space stations, from which men will both look down on their planetary home and outward toward the solar system and universe.

Just beyond near-Earth space is the Moon, and many planners are convinced that Antarctica established a pattern that may be adaptable to the Moon. In place of quick forays made with costly one-use space vehicles, a transportation system employing reusable equipment may help us establish and resupply a semipermanent lunar base. Such a base might first be built into and take advantage of a natural lunar feature. Later, with the feasibility and utility of the base made certain, one can visualize a larger domed structure formed in place to provide more convenient working and living areas. A

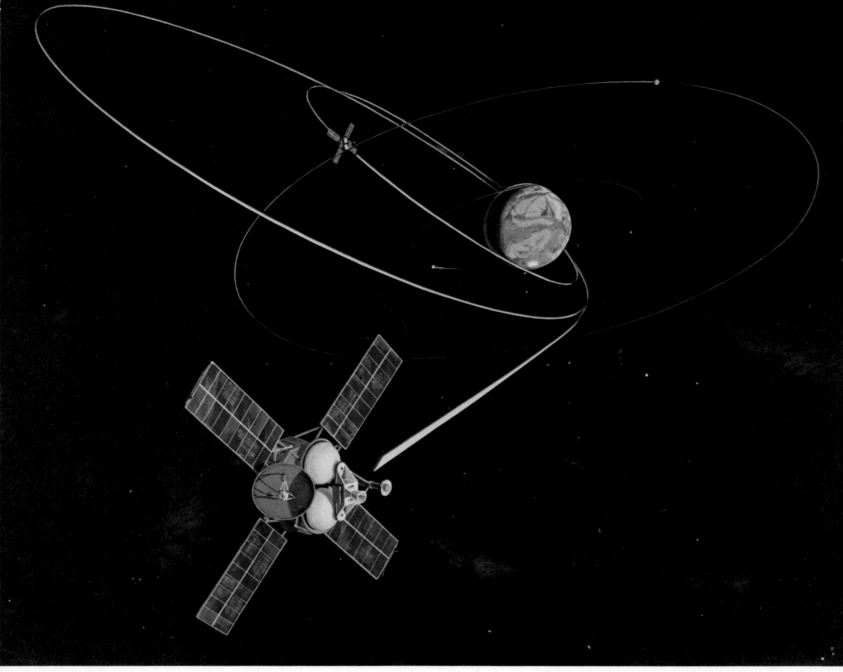

JET PROPULSION LABORATORY

Late in 1971, when two unmanned spacecraft begin an orbital reconnaissance of Mars, their orbits are to be the elongated ellipses. The lighter, more circular orbits shown are those of Deimos and Phobos, the tiny natural moons of Mars. The orbiters should record seasonal changes on the red planet.

small nuclear reactor similar to those already developed could provide power and heat. The international pattern of Antarctica might also be followed, the base being occupied by a multinational group of technically skilled and venturesome men working cooperatively to study and develop this neighbor of Earth.

But why? It is an old question, one that must have been raised when the first European settlers crossed the perilous North Atlantic. Why did settlers commit themselves to a harsh and hazardous voyage, to reach at best a howling wilderness of wild animals and savages, with brutal winters in which they might starve? Correspondingly, why

169

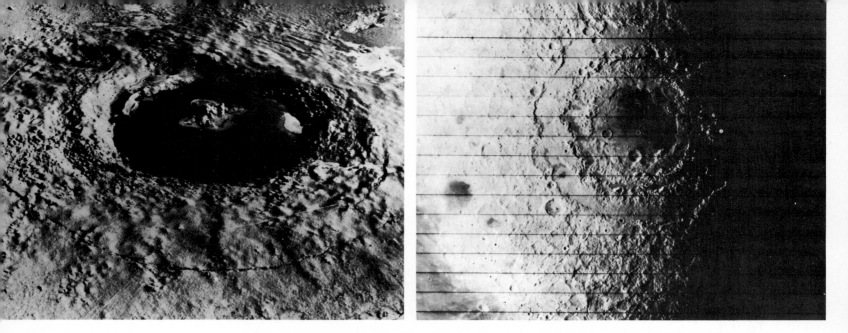

The 100-foot crater at left above was made by a dynamite explosion in water-saturated soil at Canada's Sheffield Experiment Station. At right above is a Lunar Orbiter 4 photograph of the Moon's Orientale Basin, more than 600 miles in diameter. Astrogeologists of the U.S. Geological Survey find strong parallels in the two photographs.

should we risk men and spend resources on an airless orbiting body with immense temperature extremes? Why pour money into such an expedition when there is so much that needs doing on Earth? The questions, which may some day resemble questions about what possible value could be derived from the American wilderness, beg the basic fact that man is, in the main, a rational creature who tends to work in his own self-interest. We will build and occupy bases on the Moon only after we conclude, soberly and thoughtfully, that it will be rewarding to do it.

The benefits perceived at this time would be predominantly scientific. From such a base we might gain new understanding of the origins of the double planet Earth/Moon. It might also be an international astronomical observatory of great value. It also could be a low-gravity laboratory (already fitted with an endless high-vacuum resource unobtainable on Earth), or a site periodically flooded with immense solar energy, or an economical staging stop in the further exploration of the solar system. What else the Moon will offer is presently veiled. We may be in the circumstance of the 16th-century sailors who found that America, though a dangerous wilderness, did provide a good coast off which to fish.

Planners of space exploration must work around ·

The photographic exploration of Mars has revealed remarkable similarities between parts of that planet and the Moon. The picture at left below is a Ranger 8 photo of lunar craters Ritter and Sabine, taken from an altitude of about 175 miles. At right below are frost-dusted Martian craters at the edge of the south polar cap, taken from an altitude of about 3775 miles.

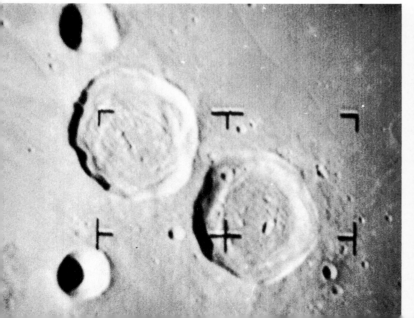

The double crater Janus, above left, is in the San Francisco volcanic field in Arizona. It consists of two vents, probably created simultaneously. A near counterpart can be seen in the lunar double crater shown at right above, photographed in the Hyginus Rille by Lunar Orbiter 5. There are many double craters on the Moon.

a complex set of constraints. The first is established by the state of the art: what technical advances can be relied on? (When Apollo was planned, some knowledgeable people were unconvinced that the mission was possible within the time allotted.) Another is the long lead time required for equipment, typically years, not months. The third constraint derives from the clockwork of the solar system. Until we can afford gross amounts of propulsive energy, we are confined to periodic launch opportunities. Finally, there is the constraint imposed on every Government-supported activity: how does it stand on the changing list of national priorities?

Plans have been developed to launch a series of unmanned spacecraft during the 1970's toward every planet in the solar system. The harvest of knowledge that will be reaped will undoubtedly be enlarged by Soviet spacecraft, for the U.S.S.R. has shown both intense interest and high competence in planetary investigation.

Early in the decade two improved Mariner spacecraft are scheduled to orbit Mars, scanning more than 70 percent of the surface. They may be able to record for the first time seasonal changes, duststorms, and the evolution of Martian clouds. By returning imagery amounting to a substantial atlas of the planet, they will aid in the selection of "interface" areas for robot landings. These are places of

The photo at left below shows a heavily cratered portion of the Moon's surface; the picture at the right below reveals a heavily cratered area on Mars, taken by Mariner 6 in 1969. But some areas of Mars are almost wholly devoid of craters, down to the limits of camera resolution, evidently as a result of some process of smoothing or filling in.

a boundary or transitional nature, of special value because they let local data be related to broader information acquired from orbit. If extraterrestrials were sending a spacecraft to Earth, they might conclude that a seacoast landing would add more meaning to prior orbital photography than would a landing in either the Sahara or in mid-Pacific.

Piecing Together a Mosaic

Knowledge of the Moon and other planets promises to be of direct benefit in piecing together a mosaic that will reveal hitherto unrecoverable information about the Earth's past. Comments J. F. McCauley of the U.S. Geological Survey:

> *. . . Trying to work out the geology of the Moon and Mars is not just an idle philosophical exercise; it's really pushing back the frontiers of the past, into those periods of time we will never be able to work out here on Earth. . . . The excellent thing about Mars is that it is between the Moon and Earth in size and density. From what we've seen from the '69 Mariner pictures, Mars looks to be a considerably more dynamic place than the Moon, but yet has many similarities to it, and is heavily cratered. What Mars is going to give us, if you will, is another point on the curve of planetary evolution—the Moon here, the Earth there, and Mars somewhere in between. From these I think we'll be able to put together a very nice picture.*

Although the first orbital photography of Mars will not match the resolution and quality already obtained of the Moon, it promises to be both better and broader than the flyby imagery obtained in 1965 and 1969. This means that we will be able to extend the highly instructive analogy studies that have been so fruitful a result of the Lunar Orbiter spacecraft.

Here as elsewhere all roads seem to curve back to Earth: we are finding more and more analogs of our own planet's features showing up on the scarred face of the Moon. The gain from such studies could be more far reaching than abstract knowledge. There is indication that ore guides—the geologic signposts used by prospectors on Earth to point to the possible presence of paydirt beneath the surface—may be revised and improved on the

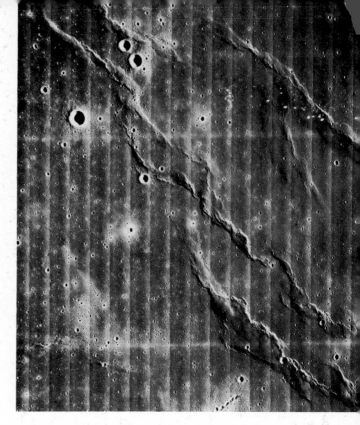

Mare ridges believed to have been created by the upwelling of lava through fissures—the same sort of volcanic action thought responsible for building 40 000 miles of midoceanic ridges on Earth—are here seen on both the Marius Hills

basis of lunar and Martian features. It is quite possible that space exploration will some day lead us to extensive new discoveries of the Earth's own metals, minerals, and ores.

A multiplanet mission, the first one attempted, is scheduled for launch in 1973, when a Mariner spacecraft will set forth to fly past both Venus and Mercury. Its closest approach to Venus will be 3300 miles. The strong pull of Venus' gravity will deflect its trajectory and sharply increase its velocity, sending the craft toward rendezvous with Mercury. The swingby or gravity-assist trajectory is a solar-system billiard shot that greatly economizes on energy, but it calls for exceptionally accurate navigation. A miss of a mile at Venus could, if uncorrected, mean a 1000-mile error at Mercury. The spacecraft will carry a restartable course-correcting rocket that can be used on both legs of the journey. Two giant new parabolic antennas, in Spain and Australia, will by then be ready to supplement the 210-foot antenna already at work in California, to track the little spacecraft with extreme precision.

In this case the rewards are high: close-in imagery of both Venus and Mercury, and the detection

region of the Moon (left above) and on Mars (above). In the Mariner 7 picture of Mars, the ridge is visible at the bottom of the scene, following a sinuous course along the bottom. In the same Mars picture, many impact craters closely resemble the

best-known impact crater in the United States, Arizona's Meteor Crater, above. At the top of the Mars photo, note a faint, double-ringed crater at top, also moonlike.

and measurement of atmospheric constituents, temperatures, magnetic fields, and planetary radiation. For a scientifically proud generation, we have a surprisingly scant understanding of these two planets.

Transformation of Venus

Venus in particular is tantalizing, since the more we have learned, the less confidently we can construct a consistent model of that opaquely shrouded world. Is the anomalous heat of Venus—far higher than its solar distance should cause—a result of the greenhouse effect alone? Is Venus instructive to Earth of the results of allowing a carbon dioxide imbalance to form in a planetary atmosphere?

Is it possible that life developed on Venus before it did on Earth and was then destroyed by a malfunction in the atmospheric mechanisms? Can we contemplate, some years hence, the concept of modifying the atmosphere of Venus, perhaps transforming it into a habitable world? Although the idea may seem bizarre, it is not unscientific, given several pyramided assumptions. Scientists are probing

the uncomfortable possibility that, without intending it, we may have already begun to modify the Earth's atmosphere. It is clearly in our own interest to learn as much as we can about the mechanisms and dynamics of planetary atmospheres other than the one overhead.

Meanwhile, somewhat simpler spacecraft are planned for exciting precursor missions: to fly outward beyond Mars, traverse the asteroid belt, and reconnoiter Jupiter. Their design will be a modification of the present Pioneer spacecraft, sophisticatedly simple mechanisms that have already shown exceptionally reliable performance. Traveling away from the Sun, the Jupiter Pioneers will carry radioisotope generators for power. They will be spin stabilized in space, turning at a leisurely five revolutions a minute. At encounter their messages will need an incredible 47 minutes of transmission time to span the half-billion miles to Earth.

Almost everything about these missions will beat out new trails. At launch the spacecraft will reach a velocity of 32 400 mph, the fastest yet. Depending on the exact trajectory selected, one spacecraft may whip around Jupiter and then loop into a solar

173

This multielement object is an engineering mockup of a Viking spacecraft, an unmanned laboratory planned to make the first U.S. soft landing on Mars. The upper half is the orbiter; the aerodynamically shaped object below contains the lander.

orbit perpendicular to the ecliptic plane, flying back again many millions of miles above the north poles of the inner planets. The other Pioneer may, after encounter, pursue a curving course that will take it out of the solar system, the first artifact of man to leave forever the domain of the Sun. The two missions are calculated to do more than contribute basic information about Jupiter; they will also assess the unknown hazards of traversing the asteroid belt and flying in deeper, blue-water space, giving us the technology and operating experience needed for more difficult voyages to come.

Knowledge about Mars, enlarged by the atlas of imagery and additional data acquired in the 1971

missions, will take a giant step forward when we launch unmanned orbiter-lander missions planned to make a detailed analysis of the Martian environment. Piercing Mars' thin atmosphere, using an aerodynamic shell, parachutes, and radar-throttled retrorockets to burn off orbital velocity and set down gently, each lander will come to rest in an area chosen to give local data most easily related to existing orbital information. Once landed and powered up, the laboratory on the surface will make measurements of pressure, temperature, wind direction, and velocity. A television eye will peer acutely at the nearby surface and also pan about the Marsscape. A mechanical arm will scoop up samples of

174

This giant steerable antenna at Goldstone, Calif., is 210 feet in diameter and sensitive enough to pick up weak signals from spacecraft half a billion miles away. Others like it are to be built in Spain and Australia, primarily in support of planetary exploration.

soil for rudimentary tests of biological activity. It is just possible that these spacecraft may bring us the first suggestive indications of some kind of radiation-resistant, water-sparing extraterrestrial life. Such a discovery would dispel forever a part of the loneliness of the human spirit.

Ambiguity is almost inseparable from scientific work at the edge of the unknown, however, and we will deal at best with probabilities. Not until more complex and versatile automatic laboratories can be deposited on the plains of Mars, and perhaps not until man himself can land there, with his powers of perception, analysis, selection, deduction, and test, will probabilities edge toward proof. The years of patient, if handicapping, sterilization of every part of every spacecraft sent toward Mars will then be of the utmost scientific importance. For all the rigors of the Martian environment, it may prove easy to seed it—biologically, to contaminate it—with fast-spreading, adaptive life of earthly origin.

On Earth we have been accustomed to think of life as precarious and somehow tender; recently, we have learned that it is both powerfully adaptive and environmentally influential. The older idea was that life could not exist until permissive conditions allowed it to thrive. Our present knowledge indicates that this was a simplification. Life displays almost an ingenuity, in its chemical and metabolic processes, in creating an environment as well as in adapting to it. Mars may be lifeless now and may never have sustained life in its past, but it seems likely that it will be a harbor for life before long.

Grand Tours

Extremely exciting opportunities open up in 1977 and 1979. They will not recur for a century and three-quarters, in the remoteness of A.D. 2152. This will be a relative positioning of the outer planets such that a spacecraft launched in September 1977, guided to fly close past Jupiter in February 1979, will gain enough swingby energy to carry it past Saturn in September of the following year, there to gain enough energy to travel thousands of millions of miles, flying past outermost Pluto in March 1986. The launch of another robot in November 1979, and also flown past Jupiter, can give us a complementary scouting of the other outer planets, passing close by Uranus in July 1985 and Neptune in November 1988.

These "Grand Tours," conceived by men and tested and refined by the calculations of electronic computers, surely deserve their descriptive title. They offer challenging problems in guidance and control, and in the design of self-repairing mechanisms that will work reliably in cold darkness for 9 unattended years. But the rewards are compellingly high for seizing this chance to make an energy- and time-saving reconnaissance of all the outer planets, which we could otherwise reach only with more powerful launch vehicles, and far longer interplanetary cruise times. Thousands of men who have gone before us—astronomers, explorers, ancient and modern scientists, philosophers, questing intelligences all—would envy us our one-in-three lifetimes chance, and approve our decision to try.

INDEX

181

182

☆ U. S. GOVERNMENT PRINTING OFFICE : 1970 O - 404-154